Angler's
Safety
and
First Aid

OUTDOOR LIFE TAKE-ALONG BOOKS

Angler's Safety and First Aid

Mark Sosin

Drawings By Tom Beecham

OUTDOOR LIFE • HARPER & ROW

NEW YORK • LONDON

Designed by Jeff Fitschen

Manufactured in the United States of America

CONTENTS

INTRODUCTION

Compared to life in the city, there are few dangers in the outdoors. Yet most of us have become accustomed to living in urban or suburban areas. The angler who spends the week behind his desk in a multi-storied office building or reports to work daily at a manufacturing plant is generally unfamiliar with life in the outdoors, even though he may take to stream or lake on the weekend.

An instant change comes over the angler who has just entered the forest or field. Like the sun bursting from the shadow of a dark cloud or an unseen hand lifting a staggering burden from the shoulders, there is a feeling of newborn life. Gone are the frustrations of work. Body and soul relax, while the mind dreams of a glistening trout in a mountain stream or a lunker largemouth lurking among lily pads. And in that unleashing of new energy lies a danger: the tendency to dispense with caution and safety in the haste to turn the dream into reality.

The key to safety is nothing more than common sense and understanding the ways of the outdoors. There's a different set of rules when you close the office door on Friday evening or climb out of the cab of your tractor trailer. But all you have to do is learn the basic rules and then apply them. If an angler plans ahead, knows what to expect, and avoids taking unnecessary risks, he can minimize the possibility of encountering hazardous situations.

Sometimes, we don't give common sense a chance to work for us or spend the extra moments required to analyze a situation before plunging into it. My excuse several years ago for one close call was that I was suffering from the impetuousness of youth.

I was exploring a section of a well-known New York State trout stream early one June and relished the idea of finding areas that were not heavily fished. My wanderings uncovered a run of the river that passed through a small gorge. Looking down from the cliff on one side, I could almost taste the trout that had to be resting near the riffles and at the tails of the deep, black pools. There was little question that the majority of anglers had to pass up this spot, since access was anything but easy.

It didn't take long to run back to the car and pick up a length of half-inch manila rope that I carried for such emergencies. A quick survey of the landscape uncovered a fallen tree near the edge. Securing the rope to the tree and tying the flyrod across my back, I lowered myself over the side and descended toward the stream. About halfway down, my ears detected the sickening sound of dry wood snapping, and before I could react I was plummeting toward the rocky shoulder of the stream.

Fortunately, I managed to get a leg under my body before toppling over backward on my head. The flyrod was smashed against the rock, and it was only luck that prevented my head from encountering the same fate. Shaken and bruised, I took several hours to work my way out of the gorge.

Anyone who has heard this story immediately asks why I didn't check the tree first before tying the line around it. The fact is that I did study the tree, but not carefully enough. I was well aware of the dangers of dead branches snapping, but my eagerness to reach these virgin trout waters dulled my senses and caused me to accept a tree as secure when further examination would have proven it to be dry and rotten.

When enthusiasm clouds the brain, it can lead to more trouble than any of us ever bargained for. As I look back on this almost tragic escapade, I have to admit that the trout fishing in other parts of the river was excellent, and there really wasn't any reason to tangle with this tough-to-reach area in the first place.

It's been said many times that "an ounce of prevention is worth a pound of cure." That is precisely the message of this book. In the first five chapters, you will become aware of numerous preventive measures that can and should be taken while you're fishing. The final segment of the book is devoted to the "pound of cure"— first-aid treatment that you should know if an accident does occur. However, keep in mind that most accidents and errors in judgment can be avoided.

1

COMMON OUTDOOR PROBLEMS

The Senses

Sight, hearing, smell, and a loosely defined "sixth sense" spell the difference between an enjoyable day afield and just time spent in other than normal surroundings. They also aid in averting an accident. Most of us are born with these vital assets, yet we fail to develop them to their full potential for the outdoors.

In the city, it's easy to hear a car approaching even above the normal din of urban life. A red traffic signal catches our eye or our sense of direction tells us that the address we seek requires a right turn. This is all part of daily living. Yet, the same individual can walk afield and be totally unaware of nature's signposts. The clues and warnings provided by nature are as glaring as the red traffic signal, but if you've never seen an automobile (no less a traffic light), you're at a disadvantage. Experience tells you that the majority of these traffic warning systems are at intersections, so you already have a pretty good idea of where to look for them.

Transfer the same thinking to the outdoors, and woods, fields, streams, lakes, and hills will take on new meaning. You'll start to hear and see things that you never dreamed existed. Learning the ways of the outdoors will take

4

time. You probably are familiar with some of the signs if you've been fishing for any length of time. The fly fisherman who persists in matching the hatch recognizes the insects on which trout are feeding. The same angler also learns to "read" water. He soon becomes familiar with the habits of his quarry and can float a fly over productive stretches. Where a current streams against the bank, he automatically knows that the water will be deeper and that the bank will be undercut, affording cover for a husky trout. Carry this one step further and he should recognize that an undercut bank offers little support to a man who happens to be standing over the lip.

Our minds don't always record what our eyes see or our ears hear. That's the problem. In the days before watches with sweep second hands, you could prove this point easily by asking the owner of the watch whether the number six on the dial was a Roman numeral six or an Arabic six. In most cases, the watch owner didn't really know, even though he glanced at his watch dozens of times a day. In reality, most men's watches at that time had a small dial with the second hand in place of the number six. There was no number six on the watch.

In the outdoors, it's necessary to force the mind to register what the eyes see or the ears hear. At first, you'll have to work at it. It won't come easily and you'll miss countless signs and signals. But, eventually, things will start falling into place and you'll be astounded by how much you missed before. All of this is the key to safety. You wouldn't plow through the passageways of a pitch-dark cave recklessly, but the average person will do just that when sunlight coats a field or filters through a woodland.

There's a trick in learning to read outdoor signs. Look for any disturbance that violates the natural pattern around you. A light breeze may be blowing across a lake, for example, bending shoreline weeds in one direction. Suddenly, you notice that a few of the weeds are moving the other way or wiggling without purpose. To the experienced eye, a fish is moving through that weedbed and a well-placed cast can reap a reward. The same thing happens when all of the ripples on a pond are going in one direction, driven by the wind. You observe a counter ripple. It's barely perceptible, but it's there. That's a fish swimming under the surface.

Fish and animals are camouflaged to survive. They often blend into the background and only a highly skilled eye can spot them. Experienced anglers use Polaroid sunglasses to peer beneath the surface of the water. The trick is to ignore the surface completely, concentrating your vision nearer the bottom. It takes concentration and thought. Again, you must look for the object that seems out of place—and it might only be part of the quarry you seek.

Not very long ago, a friend accompanied me on a day's trout fishing in a brush-lined country brook. There are some large brook and rainbow trout in that short stretch of water, but they are as skittish as you will find. If you don't give the stream a wide berth and approach quietly, the fish will disappear before you ever get within casting range.

The sound of brush and dead limbs being crushed is transmitted into the water, alerting the fish. Stand on the bank and you appear like the jolly green giant. The only sound approach is on all fours. After taking a few nice trout, I discovered that my friend was still fishless. Crawling up to a mound of dirt, I cautiously peered into the stream and could see the tail of a large trout in residence under a short log. I decided to give my friend a tip.

"Fish this log," I instructed, and then proceeded to move off to another pool. When I returned a half-hour later, I asked my friend how he fared.

"There were three trout under that log," he answered, "not just the one that you saw."

However, from my standpoint, as long as I knew there was one fish there, I believed in backing away and then fishing the spot carefully.

Learning to use your senses in the outdoors can not only help to fill a creel or game bag, but it adds to the total measure of enjoyment. At the same time, you will be learning the fundamentals of safety and will automatically circumvent situations that could lead to disaster. Danger lies in the path of the inept and those who refuse to exercise caution and common sense. Knowledge is the best preventative for accidents and inconveniences. If a fish knew a hook lurked in the bait, he wouldn't feed on it in the first place.

Work on developing the senses, and the senses will work for you!

The Elements

Part of the fun of a day spent in the outdoors is facing the elements. Sun, wind, rain, cold, and heat are present in the city as well as the countryside, but there is a difference. In the city, we can quickly avoid any of the discomforts or dangers by ducking into the nearest building or simply remaining at home. In hot weather, we can rely on a fan or air conditioning, while heating systems insure comfort on the coldest and windiest days.

If you intend to spend the day or weekend alongside your favorite trout stream, or fishing for Northern pike on a large lake, preparation is the byword. You'll have to take the proper clothing and equipment with you or they won't be available. Before we talk about clothing, let's review each of the conditions you are likely to face and the hazards involved.

Exposure to the sun. The sun can warm the body to its inner core, producing a feeling of well-being and making each day outdoors a memorable one. Just being afield on a sunlit day is a rare pleasure. But the sun can cause problems. Sunburn can be uncomfortable at best, possibly painful, and even extremely serious. Unfortunately, a well-tanned face and body is a goal coveted by many people who don't know that medical research has recently linked excessive doses of solar radiation to skin cancer. Skin cancer is becoming more common among fishing guides and professionals who are forced to endure the elements on a daily basis.

For that reason, anglers who are in the sun continually should cover exposed skin surfaces with a protective cream, to prevent the ultraviolet rays of the sun from reaching the skin. There are a number of these preparations on the market and they are available without a prescription. The lips and just under the eyes can be extremely sensitive to sun and extra care should be taken.

One aspect of the sun that newcomers to fishing frequently overlook is the reflection from the water. Even though you may be wearing a broad-brimmed hat, the sun's rays will bounce off the water and coat the face under the brim. A problem area can develop even before you begin to feel the slightest trace of a burn. And nothing can spoil the next day's fishing faster than a painful sunburn.

For that reason, it's a good idea to carry suntan lotion with you. Most people still want the tan, even though the possibility of skin cancer exists. Therefore, use a tanning lotion and expose the skin for short periods of time. An hour or two each day will quickly produce an even tan and avoid some of the discomforts of excessive exposure.

Yet the avid fisherman does not go out in the sun just to get a tan. He's busy with his avocation and the effects of sunlight are a by-product. In order to see underwater, he'll wear Polaroid sunglasses and mask the top of the glasses with the brim of a hat. He builds a tent around his eyes to keep light from filtering through around the glasses. Some anglers even use side shields on their sunglasses.

Sunglasses are a necessity for the outdoorsman. Excessively exposing the eyes to the sun can cause a loss of night vision and the eyes can also become permanently damaged. This is just as true in cold, snowy weather as it is in summer. The wise outdoorsman will drill small holes in the ends of the temple bars on his sunglasses, attach a short length of monofilament or flyline, and hang the glasses around his neck. That way, they are there when he needs them.

There are a multitude of colors and shades in which sunglasses are made. The most functional for the outdoorsman is either a true color or a light tan. The light tan in a Polaroid lens has been found to be the best for spotting fish in the water. And remember, the sun doesn't have to be shining brightly to require the use of sunglasses. Often the glare from the water is enough to warrant their use. I've worn my Polaroids in the rain so I could spot fish underwater.

Problems with wind. In addition to making casting difficult, wind can be a real problem when you're fishing. Of course, a great deal depends on the velocity of the wind, but under certain circumstances, even a light breeze can cause trouble. Meteorologists have worked out a wind-chill factor: the effect of wind on temperature. That light breeze on a cold day can be just enough to make you start to shiver, because even a wind of only a couple of knots is more than sufficient to speed up the cooling process.

There's not much anyone can do about wind, but there are a few precautions that should be

The author wears a broad-brimmed hat and polarized sunglasses with side shields while fishing. The hat shades the eyes and the polarized glasses protect them against the sun's glare.

taken. If the wind is fairly strong, you can develop a windburn (similar to sunburn) and it's equally painful. Guard against this by applying a cream or lotion to the skin. For wind, something as simple as Vasoline will do the job. And don't forget to apply a lip balm to your lips. Wind will cause them to dry out quickly and either blister or swell.

On a gusty day, the woods can hide certain dangers. That's the time when those "widow makers"—dead limbs—plummet from tall trees. If you're camping, you shouldn't pitch a tent under a tree anyway, but the rule applies doubly when it's windy.

Then, there's the story of the small-boat angler who had no trouble rowing and fishing along the shoreline on a windy day, because the wind was at his back. When he tried to return to camp, however, it became a different tale. More than one angler has been forced to beach a boat and walk back because the wind was too strong. This, by the way, is the technique you *should* use if a sudden wind whips a lake into a froth. Get the boat or canoe in the lee, and if necessary, don't hesitate to beach it. Wind can be a cruel enemy.

Protection against rain. Someone was once credited with saying that the problem with rain was that it became uncomfortable until you were thoroughly drenched; then it didn't matter to you. I can't go along with this statement, although it does stress a point. A year ago, Billy Pate and I were fishing the jungle rivers of Nicaragua. It was supposed to be the dry season, but torrential downpours occurred at least a half-dozen times daily. In fact, if we hesitated in putting on our rain suits, it was too late. The air temperature was well up in the eighties.

During one shower, I decided to forget about the rain suit. After all, perspiration kept you wet constantly. As the shower subsided, the sun burned down and my clothes dried quickly. Yet, in spite of the warmth, I was still cold. Evapora-

Keeping dry is an important part of being comfortable in the outdoors, and comfort is a major factor in safety practices. A pair of waterproof boots and a rain suit are all you need to stay dry. The rain suit top also serves as a windbreaker.

tion is a cooling process and all of that moisture leaving my skin and garments caused my body to chill beyond the comfortable point. There was a marked difference between the evaporation of moisture after removing a rain suit and the evaporation needed to dry out my clothing.

In addition, walking or working in wet clothes or footwear can be an irritating experience. It's not serious in normal temperatures, of course, but it can detract from the pleasures at hand. That's one reason why it makes sense to keep a rain suit handy for sudden showers or day-long deluges. At the same time, unless it's warm enough and convenient enough to go without shoes, waterproof footwear makes sense.

When temperatures drop, water can deprive clothing of its insulating qualities and it will cease to trap air effectively. Then rain can become a real problem and put a quick end to a day in the outdoors. Of course, if you don't have rain gear with you and are overtaken by a shower, you can always seek shelter. However, there's a minor danger from electrical storms, particularly if you decide to stand under the only tree in an open field or the tallest tree in a woodland lot.

Cold-weather hazards. Ice fishing is becoming extremely popular across the northern tier of states, and each year more anglers brave the cold of winter to pursue their favorite sport through the ice. Temperatures might try to pull the thermometer off the wall, but as long as the sportsman is dressed for the occasion, he can have a good time in the outdoors. During the winter steelhead run in the Pacific Northwest, many outdoorsmen are willing to forego the comforts of a warm fireplace to fish for the great sea-run rainbow trout. Even in the more temperate latitudes of the country, trout fishermen frequently encounter snow showers on opening day, with flyline freezing in the guides and wet hands suffering the pain of severe chilling.

One of the greatest dangers of cold-weather fishing is frostbite. Medical men tell us that frostbite is very similar to a burn, resulting in death of tissue. Frostbite usually affects the extremities first, such as hands, feet, and parts of the face, because these are the more difficult areas for the body to heat.

This is a situation where the wind-chill factor can truly come into play. The average outdoor enthusiast considers frostbite to be a product of the far North, seldom expecting to find it in the middle latitudes. However, we know that even a light wind can have the same effect as extremely low temperatures, and frostbite can occur before the victim realizes it.

Frostbite is also another argument for keeping dry during cold weather. Remember that evaporation is a cooling process and as skin temperatures drop, the risk of frostbite increases. How susceptible you are to frostbite depends on your circulatory system and whether you perspire a great deal.

Your first clue to frostbite is a tingling sensation and numbness of a particular body extremity. As the symptoms increase, you may find that the skin becomes flushed, turning extremely red or purplish red. It may even start to burn, or perhaps itch, and if it is not attended to immediately, will turn white and feeling will be lost.

It's important to recognize the possibility of frostbite and take appropriate precautions to prevent it. Keeping a pair of wet boots on for several hours on a cold day is a perfect way to contract frostbite.

Cold temperatures also pose other hazards. For one thing, you're going to be wearing several layers of clothing and you should recognize that you cannot maneuver your body as easily or as quickly. Basically, your muscles are going to be slightly stiffer and the extra clothing will be bulky. You simply won't be able to jump as far or be as agile as you are in summer garb, so consider this as you negotiate fields, woodlands, and obstacles in your path.

The weight of the extra attire will also tax your muscles faster and you'll find that fatigue sets in more quickly. Gauge your forward progress so you'll have reserve energy to work your way back. At the same time, anyone who lives in snow country knows how much more energy it takes to walk in even light snow. And, of course, snowbirds also realize that icy patches can be slippery. Footing is not as sure as it is on average turf—another point to consider in pursuing your avocation during the winter or early spring months.

Extreme heat. Move closer to the equator or wait for the summer sun to warm the land and similar problems will be caused by extreme heat. In fact, heat can be just as dangerous as cold. It can also be exhausting. For that reason, a man with a heart condition or the weekend out-doorsman who is not used to strenuous exercise must be careful. He should take frequent rest periods and avoid strenuous activity during the heat of the day.

The human body cools itself through the process of perspiring. Perspiration is composed basically of water and dissolved chemical salts. In fact, about 60 percent of the body's weight is water or water-based fluids. Although a man can survive for long periods without food, he cannot last very long without water.

The critical aspect is that it doesn't take very much water loss before you start feeling the effects. Efficiency shows a marked decline. You become tired. Dizziness and headaches can oc-cur. Pulse increases, the skin flushes, and you may even feel nauseous. These are only the first symptoms. As the body continues to suffer from lack of water, saliva may stop, speech may be-come slurred, vision may be blurred, hearing may be lost, and a host of other symptoms may develop.

Realistically, unless you are in an extreme circumstance, concern should be centered around the normal intake of water for hot climates. It is vital to realize that you must have water and plenty of it when you are perspiring freely. The water loss must be replaced quickly and continuously. Recognizing this fact, you should actually force yourself to drink more water than you usually would when the weather is hot and you are doing anything other than sitting quietly in the shade. Even then, you'll have to increase water intake slightly.

Salt intake is just as critical as water. Researchers have done considerable work in the area of the relationship between salts and water in the body and suggest that you also increase the intake of salt when you increase the intake of water. If you require a salt-free diet, or have encountered problems with the relationship between salt and water in your body, consult your physician before venturing into a warmer climate.

For most of us, increased salt intake can be achieved through the use of more salt on our food, salt tablets, or both. Every angler, except those with special problems, should carry a bottle of salt tablets in his fly vest or tacklebox. One or two tablets taken periodically with plenty of water will restore the needed salts and fluids. The ones I prefer combine dextrose (sugar) with the salt and seem to restore energy faster than the tablets without dextrose. Some people may find that salt tablets make them nauseous. In that case, they should consult their family doctor.

Increasing the water and salt intake should be an automatic procedure in warm climates. You should begin before you feel you need it. And you'll discover that you require more water in hot weather to do the same amount of exercise or type of fishing, so prepare for it in advance and carry plenty of liquids with you.

Fishermen may find themselves cruising in a boat and perspiring freely at the same time. The motion of the boat creates a breeze and the skin feels dry. What really is happening is that perspiration is evaporating almost instantly, but they are still suffering water loss. This is one aspect of hot-weather fishing that you must remedy before you start to feel the effects.

Clothing

The serious fisherman is much more concerned with the functional aspects of clothing than with its appearance. Each item of apparel serves a specific purpose and should be selected on that basis. Manufacturers in recent years have made great strides both in the design of outdoor clothing and in the materials used. Lightweight permanent-press clothing dries quickly and will retain an unwrinkled look even after hard use. For winter wear, new filler material coupled with wind-resistant outer fabrics insure warmth while providing light weight.

Every angler has his own preference in clothes, but as a general rule they should fit somewhat loosely to provide freedom of movement. You'll also discover that tight-fitting clothes are warmer in the summer because air cannot circulate and colder in winter because of the lack of dead air space.

As a basic guide, it is far better to dress in layers of clothing rather than to rely on one heavy jacket. An angler is usually extremely active in the pursuit of his sport, and activity generates warmth. With layers of clothing, he can easily add or remove items to adjust to conditions and varying temperatures. Of course, in warm climates clothing should be extremely lightweight and should absorb perspiration readily and dry quickly.

In cold weather, it is important to concentrate on keeping the extremities warm. A hat can be vital, since it has been estimated that about 25 percent of the body's heat loss dissipates through the head. If there's a chance of frostbite, don't forget to keep the ears covered as well. You'll also discover that two pairs of gloves—a warm lining and outer wind-resistant shell—are warmer than a single pair. And in extreme cold, mittens are warmer than gloves.

It's also been proven that if you can keep the kidneys warm, the body has a better chance of staying warmer. For that reason, hip length jackets are superior to those that stop at the waist. Especially in a boat, a wind-resistant jacket or parka is particularly valuable. It needn't be more than a tightly woven shell. In fact, a number of anglers use the top from a rainsuit as a windbreaker.

If you're going to do any type of walking, particularly through fields and brush, you should have a pair of comfortable shoes or boots that are thoroughly broken in and support your feet. Crossing swampy areas or even wet fields requires waterproof boots, since it can be extremely uncomfortable to walk any distance with wet socks and boots. In cold weather this requirement is even more valid. You could contract frostbite, known as "immersion foot" in this case.

Perhaps the best rule is to select your outdoor clothing as carefully as you would your fishing tackle. Purchases should not be made at random, but rather as part of a careful plan designed to outfit you for your current and future needs.

And don't forget the weight factor. It's much easier and less tiring to work in featherweight clothing than it is to be burdened by the old type of mackinaw.

Insects

If you're going to spend any amount of time in the outdoors, sooner or later insects will be a problem. Since most of the common varieties breed in wet areas, the fisherman is a frequent victim.

Modern science has concocted chemical repellants that do a good job in aborting the mission of mosquitos, blackflies, no-see-ums, deerflies, and other outdoor pests. There are a number of brands on the market and each sportsman eventually comes up with the one that works best for him.

You can buy these preparations in the form of a lotion or in an aerosol can for spraying. In country where the insect problem is acute, you might want both kinds. The spray can is ideal for clothing and areas difficult to cover with a lotion.

It is extremely important to tuck pants legs into socks or tape them around your ankles. The same procedure should be used to secure the cuffs on your shirt and the collar around your neck. It goes without saying that long-sleeved shirts are a strong ally. In the extreme North where blackflies are a plague, you might have to resort to head netting and gloves as well. There are a number of backwoods remedies, but most of them will keep you from being

Insects are not only a nuisance in the bush but the bites of some can lead to illness. Tape clothing over ankles and wrists to prevent insects from crawling underneath. Then spray a repellant on the clothing and the exposed skin. Also spray the inside of your hat and the neckerchief.

accepted socially by the other members of the fishing party.

You might as well make up your mind that in spite of the protective measures you employ, at least one insect will score a direct hit. There are a number of anti-inflammatory hormones that can be obtained on your physician's prescription that can eliminate the itching and irritation quickly.

In some parts of the country, chiggers will be on hand to wage full-scale war. You won't feel them bite or even work their way into the skin as they leap from grass or greenery. However, by the next morning, you'll know they are there. They'll show up as red dots on the skin and the itching can be severe. Precautionary measures include a bath at night with strong soap or washing in salt water. If the insect has already penetrated the skin, a small dab of clear nail polish over the red spot will cut off the air supply by sealing the skin. However, this should be done with care because it could lead to infection. Try a few dabs, and if you have no ill effects, continue the treatment.

Other sections of the country are noted for ticks. A tick has the nasty habit of burying its head in the skin, and if you try to pull it out, the head will probably remain—which could lead to infection. Instead, the best technique is to dab some gasoline or alcohol over the tick, and it should come out. Ticks are sometimes hard to locate, so have your fishing partner check you over and you do the same for him at the end of the day's fishing.

Although the insects mentioned above are a nuisance, they are not generally dangerous. However, bees, wasps, and hornets are. Before you shake your head in disbelief, it might come as a surprise to know that more people in the United States die each year from bee stings than from rattlesnake bites. In fact, the venom of a bee on a drop-for-drop basis is equally as potent as the venom from a rattlesnake, the difference being that a rattlesnake obviously injects a greater quantity of venom.

Of course, most people are not seriously affected by a bee sting, but as an outdoorsman, you should be alert to what might happen. Most of us know that the honey bee loses its stinger when it bites, but wasps, yellow jackets, and hornets do not, allowing them to strike repeatedly.

Avoid bees and keep alert for nests. Walking into a hornets' nest, as the saying goes, can be a most disconcerting (if not dangerous) experience. In the event you do, plunging into the nearest water is as good a remedy as any—providing there is some nearby.

The point to remember is that bee stings can be fatal. A great deal depends on the individual and the number of stings. Your job is to watch the victim carefully. If the reaction is more than just a small painful swelling—and particularly if he shows signs of shortness of breath or distress of another type—get him to a doctor as fast as possible.

In the course of your outdoor adventures, you could run into dozens of other types of insects ranging from black widow spiders to scorpions and even certain types of caterpillars that might cause a problem. Remember that each of us may react to an insect bite in a different way, and even though the same sting or bite doesn't affect you, it might affect another member of your family or your fishing partner. The best guideline is not to take a chance. Leave insects alone, no matter how pretty or unusual they might look. If someone should be bitten, don't ignore it.

Snakes

Almost everyone is afraid of snakes, yet if you tried to uncover the reason, you would be hard pressed to do so. Perhaps it is the natural fear that surrounds something we don't understand. Whatever the reason, there is a natural tendency to destroy things we cannot comprehend and snakes have been the victims of unwarranted attacks by some outdoorsmen. Snakes are a vital part of nature's scheme and should be avoided.

In the United States, there are four basic species of poisonous snakes: the rattlesnake, copperhead, cottonmouth water moccasin, and coral snake. The first three are pit vipers, named because of the deep pit between their eyes and nostrils. Pit vipers strike quickly by burying a pair of fangs in the skin and injecting a dose of poison. The poison of the pit vipers attacks and destroys local tissues. Saliva from the snake's mouth also contains an anticoagulant that prevents the blood from clotting normally.

The coral snake is different. It is extremely dangerous and does not let go after the strike, holding on to the skin and sinking its fangs deeper. Poison from the coral snake, like that of the cobras, does not affect local tissues but moves into the nerves.

Fortunately, snakebite is a relatively rare occurrence in this country, and on an average there are less than thirty fatalities a year from poisonous snakes. Most of the few fatalities involve older people with other weakening illnesses and small children who simply don't have enough tissue area to dissipate the poison.

If you understand that a snake is more afraid of you than you are of it, you're on the right track. The problem occurs when a sportsman inadvertently surprises or corners a snake. If you were cornered by someone or something that you believed would harm you, you would probably react in a violent and unnatural way. It's no different with snakes. Nonpoisonous snakes, of which there are over one hundred varieties in the United States, will also bite if surprised or provoked.

For purposes of discussion, we'll talk about the poisonous varieties, but the same rules apply to any species of snake. Rattlesnakes are the easiest to recognize because of the string of "rattles" on their tail. Colorations may vary, but there's no mistaking those rattles. And don't believe that you can always hear a rattlesnake before it strikes.

The cottonmouth makes its home in swampy areas, on the banks of streams and rivers, and on the banks of ponds or lakes. You would be hard pressed to find one any distance from this habitat. They are difficult to recognize, but the head will be angular instead of round and you may be able to see the pit.

Copperheads have a unique aspect to their coloration, which will vary. The blotches on the back will be narrower at the middle of the back than on the sides. All other snakes, both poisonous and nonpoisonous, have the widest part of the blotches across the middle of the back.

The coral snake looks very much like the scarlet king snake (a nonpoisonous variety). On the coral, the nose is black and the red and yellow bands are next to each other. All other snakes in the United States are nonpoisonous. And you may be interested to learn that Maine, Hawaii, and Alaska do not have any of the poisonous varieties.

Preventing snakebite is not difficult, but it does require alertness. Usually, just the normal amount of noise you make while moving through a field or woods is enough to frighten most snakes. However, it is well to realize that most snakebites occur on the hands or legs, indicating that the victim either walked or probed where he shouldn't.

In territory known for an abundance of snakes, the best protection is a pair of high boots. You'll also find that loose-fitting trousers are better than shorts or tight pants, since the snake may strike the cloth and not the skin. The main idea in avoiding snakes is to keep your eyes open. Learn the type of terrain they frequent and you'll have a clue to where you might expect them. For example, stepping over a log blindly is a prime way to incur the wrath of a snake. Reaching up on a ledge without looking first can also bring disaster. Trout fishermen wading in a stream often probe blindly along the bank for a hand-hold to help them climb ashore. In snake country, that could mean trouble if you don't scout the area first.

None of the snakes in our country will stalk or purposely attack a man. The problem develops when they feel cornered or trapped. All of us have heard stories of anglers who find a rattlesnake along a trail and then turn around to discover that another one has taken up residence behind them. This is simply coincidence rather than part of an attack plan as some people believe.

The best medicine for snakes is to leave them alone and walk around them. If you can't circumvent the snake, use your fishing rod to carefully convince the snake to seek other habitat for the moment. A long stick will do the same job, but don't kill the snake! The only time a snake should be killed is if someone is bitten. Then it's important to bring the snake back (if you can) for positive identification.

Wild Fruits and Foods

The North American continent contains an abundance of wild fruits and foods that are not only palatable (and sometimes extremely tasty), but nourishing as well. However, unless you can readily identify a particular food or you are in an emergency situation, the best policy is to avoid eating wild plants at random. The human body can go without food for a long time as long as it has an adequate supply of fresh water.

Of course, wild fruits can be delicious, but before you pick and eat them, identify them positively. Make certain you avoid mushrooms since some species contain poison. This is one plant that must be positively identified.

Experts also offer a couple of other suggestions worth remembering. They caution against eating any plant or fruit that produces a milky substance or fluid. You might pass up the exception or two to the rule, but in the long run you'll come out ahead. These specialists also claim that any food that persists in burning or stinging the mouth after it has been thoroughly cooked should be discarded.

The point to remember is that identification should be made before you ingest wild foods. In an extreme situation (and remember you can go several days without food and not feel the effects), you can eat practically anything that walks, crawls, flies, swims, or wriggles. The meat of rattlesnakes, and of other poisonous creatures, is safe, since the poison is carried in a sac and not throughout the body of the reptile.

Noted wildlife photographer Les Blacklock spends long days afield stalking subject material. There is seldom time to eat during these working sessions and Les has come up with a simple recipe he calls "Chorp." It's nothing more than bits of chocolate, peanuts, and raisins mixed together in a plastic bag. The combination will keep well for days and even weeks, and it can be carried in your fishing vest for those times when hunger starts to cloud your mind. Chorp is full of instant energy; you can easily eat a handful or two while fishing or walking.

Poison Ivy, Sumac, and Oak

Poison ivy, sumac, and oak contain an oil in the leaves that irritates the skin of many people. Not everyone is susceptible, but most of us who are find out early in life. The commonest way of contracting an irritation of the skin from these plants is to brush against them, but the oil can also be transmitted by smoke from a fire that is burning these plants. Since it is an oil that does the damage, it is possible to contract poison ivy, sumac, or oak by touching the skin of an animal or person who has been brushed with the oil.

The best advice is to learn to identify these plants and avoid them. Poison ivy is found almost everywhere in the United States, while sumac is limited to the East and oak to the West.

The rash is actually a legion of tiny blisters in the skin and there are varying remedies for it, none of which seem to work as quickly as the victim would like. Calamine lotion, available in any drugstore, is the standard. Some skin lotions such as caladryl and surfadil combine the features of calamine with an antihistamine.

If you are susceptible to the oil of one of these plants, it's best to consult your physician beforehand and carry a supply of the recommended medicine with you. In the last couple of years, drugs have been marketed that are touted to build up an immunity to poison ivy and similar plants. Some are taken orally and others administered via injections. Although they do seem to work in some cases, there is no evidence at this time that they will build total immunity.

The Hazards of Fire

In a lifetime, most of us will never see the devastating effect of a forest fire at the height of its reign. The expression "spread like wild-fire" is based on fact and not fiction. A man in prime condition cannot outrun a fire if a good wind is blowing and fanning the flames.

As you travel the world of the outdoors, you should be aware of what to do if you encounter a forest fire. Fires start small, but spread rapidly. If the fire is tiny, you may try to put it out; but unless you can gain on it quickly, seek professional help as fast as you can.

The greatest danger to the fisherman comes from being downwind of a major conflagration. You can usually hear a forest fire quite a distance away. The roar is devastating and you should be able to smell smoke and see the glow. When that happens, forget your fishing and concentrate on getting out of there as fast as you can. Don't make the mistake of believing the fire is still a good distance from you. It's amazing how fast that fire can travel, and it can jump firebreaks and bodies of water if the wind is strong enough.

Depending on the proximity of the fire, you may or may not be able to get in front of it. If the fire seems to be gaining on you, the preferred move is to try to outflank it. Remember, it will be driven by the wind, so if you can circle and get upwind, you have a chance. However, it's well to keep in mind that sudden wind shifts are not uncommon and you might think you've reached safety only to find the fire working toward you again.

If you can't outrun or outflank the fire, your best chance is to find a relatively large body of water and submerge. Narrow and shallow creeks could heat up tremendously and should only be used as a last resort.

The important consideration is to be aware of the ravages caused by forest fires so that you can get out of the way instantly and also help to prevent them by exercising care and judgment with campfires, matches, and cigarettes.

A Bad Heart

The fact that an angler has a bad heart seldom destroys the love for the outdoors that has been nurtured over the years. In many cases, people with heart trouble are permitted to fish, although it may be on a limited basis.

If you presently have heart trouble or suspect that you do, tell your physician about your love for the outdoors and ask him just what you can and cannot do. Then, follow his advice to the letter. If you have a constant fishing companion, be sure to let him know about your illness, and make the facts clear to anyone else with whom you might be fishing. Then, set your own pace and don't worry about helping with the heavy chores such as launching a boat or packing a canoe for portage. Your friends will understand, be only too glad to do the work themselves, and you can be certain they're happy to have you with them. And, if you're worried about pulling your share of the load, you'll discover a number of chores that don't require much energy that you can take over.

2

HIKING IN

Unless you know a spot where you merely have to drive your car alongside a body of water, roll the window down, poke a rod out, and catch fish, you're going to have to do some walking. For most of us, this entails shouldering all of our gear and marching across a field or woodland to the side of the stream or shore of the lake. Once we get there, we're seldom satisfied with the first spot and proceed to work our way toward greener pastures.

Preparing for a Walk

If you do a great deal of fishing, you've probably worked this aspect out in detail. Preparations should start long before you set off for the day. The trout fisherman who prefers a flyrod soon learns that practically all of his tackle (except rod and reel) can be stored in the pockets of a fly vest. All he need do is don the vest and he is fully equipped.

The experienced backpacker has trained his mind to think in terms of ounces rather than pounds. Even the ounces add up quickly, and if you can eliminate a few in several areas, you've lightened your load considerably.

Once you've organized your tackle, you can then decide on the number of rods and reels you're going to take. Keep in mind that if you are fishing on foot, the goal is to be mobile. You don't want to worry about being confined to the area where you deposit the load. Instead, you should be able to carry everything needed in your pockets, in a bag, or on your back.

A number of fishermen are now rigging up backpacks with frames to carry their gear. Waders and a heavy jacket can be lashed over the top where they are high on the shoulders. The secret of backpacking is to keep the weight high on the shoulders. Otherwise, it feels as if you're dragging a sack of potatoes.

Speaking of waders, if you have to walk a considerable distance, it's much better to carry them with you rather than put them on at the car and then try to walk. If you've ever hiked in waders, you know exactly what I mean. A good pair of walking shoes or boots are far more practical and they will support your ankles as you stride across rough terrain. In situations where you don't have to walk far, you may decide to do it in hip boots or waders.

Even if it's fairly cold, you're going to generate a great deal of energy by walking, so dress accordingly. You should be just a little cold at the start. Start to shed clothing before you really think it's necessary, donning it again once you stop. If it's really cold, you might only want to open your jacket when you start, but keep in mind that you're going to be more uncomfortable if you work up a sweat and then have to stand around.

Starting Out

Most trips to a trout stream or a hidden lake start by negotiating a fence. If there's a gate a short distance away, by all means use it. However, if you're as lucky as I am, you'll find that the gates are some distance away and you have to negotiate the fence. This is not difficult if you study the situation for a moment. One point worth remembering is that a fence marks private property and you should respect both the fence and the property. This simply means that you shouldn't try to bend the fence down, rip out a fence post, or commit similar breaches of etiquette that spoil it for other sportsmen.

Even barbed wire can be crossed without incident. Start by piling all of the gear near the fence on the same side you're on. If there are two of you, the object is to get one man through and then transfer the gear to him. But sportsmen seem to get into trouble the minute they are faced with barbed wire. The barbs can surely cause nasty wounds, but they are more likely to tear clothing or put a rip in a pair of waders.

Realizing this, the best policy is to remove those items that could become torn and spoil your fishing. Most fences have plenty of room between the ground and the bottom strand of wire. The easiest way is to crawl on your back, looking up at the bottom strand. You can then ease it past your body and clothing without mishap. This is also the way to cross a fence if you're by yourself.

In snake country, make certain you probe

With his fly vest removed and hanging on a post, a fisherman navigates a barbed-wire fence. Instead of springing the tiers of wire and climbing through, the correct technique is to work under the bottom strand on your back.

around the crossing point with a stick unless the ground is relatively bare and you can see every portion of it.

Once on the other side, it is merely necessary to shoulder the equipment and be on your way. The fence is left undamaged and your clothing should be intact. If it's going to be a close passage and you're walking in waders, don't hesitate to remove them. It might delay you a moment longer, but you won't chance tearing the waders.

The first rule in walking is to set a pace that is comfortable for you and the members of your party. If the walk is going to be a tough one, rest for short periods at frequent intervals. You'll find that this is much better than walking until you're exhausted and then resting for prolonged periods.

In all likelihood, you know the route to take because you have been there before. However, if the territory is new to you and you are following someone's directions, take a moment periodically to check the route back. Many anglers plunge across fields, through wooded lots, and never bother to look behind them. If they did, they might be able to spot some landmarks or at least get a general idea of what the land looks like from the other direction. Should there be the least bit of doubt, carry a compass with you and a topographical map. If you don't have a compass and the sun is shining, try to fix the general direction in your mind.

In rugged terrain you will tend to glue your eyes to the ground at every step. Reaching your goal or finding your way back may be difficult unless you periodically look up and take your bearings. Otherwise, you could walk miles out of the way. If there is a distant object that stands out distinctly in the direction you intend to travel, focus on it. Then, you merely have to raise your head periodically to ascertain whether you're still on course. You can do the same thing with cloud formations for short periods of time, but remember that clouds move and the formations change, so exercise caution in this regard.

It's impossible to anticipate every type of terrain you will cover in your wanderings to find better fishing holes, but there are certain basic rules you should keep in mind. Although science tells us that a straight line is the shortest distance between two points, and it can be proved mathematically, the theorem doesn't always hold true in the outdoors. You're not flying as the proverbial crow does, but walking, and it is sometimes easier and less time consuming to walk around an obstacle. So plot your course carefully, considering the energy expended and the risks involved in crossing marginal terrain.

Open fields are seldom a problem unless the area becomes swampy. Then it may pay to take the long (and dry) way around. In hiking through wooded areas, keep some of these points in mind. You're going to be carrying a fishing rod and you can bet it will catch on every stray branch unless you do something about it. Make sure the hook or lure is secured near the butt if the rod is rigged, and that the line lies tightly along the rod. Instead of carrying the rod with the tip in front of you, reverse the procedure. Hold the rod butt and the reel in your hand, and let the tip of the rod trail behind you. You'll discover that it will tangle with the tree limbs far less frequently and that you can walk through rough brush without difficulty.

Woodsmen learned a long time ago that it is much less fatiguing to walk in a relaxed manner through brush and tree limbs than to try to fight your way through. Don't go out of your way to push limbs aside with force. Instead, make an opening with your hands just large enough to let you through. If you are not the first man in line, keep a respectable distance so that if a limb is inadvertently released it won't hit you in the face.

Rod tips can be broken easily while an angler is walking through the woods. The best method of carrying a rod in heavy brush is to hold it with the reel in front and the tip behind you. You'll find that the tip does not snag very often, and if it does, it won't bend and break.

Deadfalls and logs are another hazard to the fisherman hiking in. If possible, walk around a deadfall. Accidents happen when you step on one and it collapses under your weight, or you lose your footing and slip into the tangled maze of branches. Don't stand on logs or step on them. They may not be anchored as securely

When walking through the woods, it's better to walk around deadfalls and logs than to climb over them. Standing on a log can cause the log to collapse or you can slip and sustain an injury.

as you think they are and you could take a nasty spill. In fact, just a slight movement may cause you to react suddenly, to lose your balance and sustain a back injury, sprained ankle, or muscle pull.

In rocky areas, recognize the danger of loose rocks sliding underfoot. At the same time, if you're walking under a rocky ledge or cliff, be alert for signs of falling rock. A little dirt sliding down should be all the warning you need. And if you must hop from boulder to boulder, a bit of moss or slime can spell disaster. Make sure of your footing and landing area before you leap.

Wildlife

Part of the fun of being in the outdoors is observing wildlife in its natural habitat. In time, you'll accidentally see your fair share, but if the terrain isn't too tough, keep your eyes and ears open. You can bet that wildlife of every description is anxious to avoid you—at least most of the time. However, like snakes, animals will react when cornered or surprised.

Most bears will disappear at the sight, sound, or smell of man. But the bear—any bear—is a wild and dangerous animal. Unfortunately, the American public has tended to associate all bears with the image created by Smokey or Gentle Ben. They automatically assume a bear is a tame, lovable creature instead of recognizing it as a dangerous and wild animal.

The more common species is the black bear, which survives in some areas by foraging in garbage cans or accepting handouts. Particularly in our National Parks where hunting is prohibited, bears can quickly lose their fear of man. This makes them even more dangerous. Instead of fleeing at man's approach, they begin to welcome it. And, if they don't get what they want or aren't satisfied, they may attack. As a fisherman, you probably won't be spending your time at a roadside rest area feeding bears. However, you should know that a bear is totally unpredictable. A black bear can be trouble and a grizzly can be even more trouble. Grizzlies seldom venture into the more populated areas, preferring to live a natural life away from people in remote sections.

The National Park Service advises outdoorsmen to make their presence known in bear country. You can do this by wearing a small bell on your clothing that will make noise as you walk. Pebbles in a can will serve the same purpose. Loud talking also seems to help. Yet park rangers warn that this is not a foolproof method.

It's important to let the bear know you are there. Don't try to sneak up on a bear or even around one. If you should spot a bear on the trail ahead of you, make a wide detour around it. If possible, try to stay upwind of the bear so it will quickly gain your scent and know you are there. Should you discover that there is no easy way around the bear, be patient and wait until the bear has moved on. Above all, don't try to chase a bear out of your path.

Remember this about bears: They can be extremely dangerous if you approach them too closely or startle them, especially when they have lost their fear of man, and when a sow has cubs with her. Since you can never tell if a bear has lost its fear of man, it doesn't pay to take chances. There might be one bear that hasn't read the book and doesn't know how it's supposed to react.

What happens if you're suddenly confronted by a bear? Answers to this question are not clearcut because every animal is an individual. There are guidelines, based on the experience of others, that are worth remembering. You're going to have to judge each situation individually, but here are a few things to keep in mind:

You can't outrun a bear (especially over rough ground), so don't try. Running can excite the animal and turn a static situation into a dangerous one. The National Park Service recommends that if the bear is not aggressive, stand your ground, but don't move forward. Bears cannot see well and might want to get close enough to take a look at the source of the noise they heard. While you're trying to remain calm, you should be scouting for a tree to climb. Look for one without low limbs, with the upper limbs spaced for easy climbing. You're going to climb high and you're going to climb faster than you ever did before.

At times, a bear will rise on its hind quarters —a menacing sight to say the least. Some experts suggest you try to talk to the bear in soft, reassuring tones. It may sound like folly, but it has worked in the past. However, they go on to advise that you'd better be scouting a

If you find yourself confronted by a bear, you can usually back away and give the animal time and room to move off. However, if you are attacked and cannot reach a tree, the best technique is to fall to the ground, draw your knees up to your chest, cover your neck and face, and remain motionless. The bear may pass you by.

tree for climbing at the same time. Under no circumstances should you throw something at the bear, wave your arms wildly, or intimidate or threaten the animal in any way.

What do you do if the bear really becomes aggressive and starts to attack? Never having been attacked by a bear, I can only tell you what the National Park Service recommends. They suggest you consider the distance to that tree you selected. If you think you can make it, give it a try. Only keep in mind that a bear is twice as fast as you might suspect. Otherwise, your only alternative is to play dead. The National Park people suggest lying on your stomach or your side with your legs drawn up to your chest. Hands should be placed over the back of the neck for added protection and your face should be turned under.

It's going to take extreme courage to lie motionless, but experts feel that is your only chance. Some bears have passed by people in this position without harming them, while others have slapped once or twice, causing only minor injuries. As the bear is advancing toward you, and before you drop to the ground or try to get up a tree, you may explore some delaying tactics. Bears are curious and they may stop to investigate an item you drop on the ground such as a parka, camera, fishing rod, or anything else that is handy.

The only time you should try to harass a bear is if it is attacking someone. Then you can throw sticks or stones at it, yell loudly, and do anything to divert the bear from its victim.

If you happen upon a sow with cubs or merely see the cubs, you're already in a dangerous situation. Sows will attack without provocation. You can either scamper up a tree, or if the bear hasn't seen you, carefully work your way out of the area.

Many fishermen enjoy camping at stream or lakeside for a few days of prime sport. In bear country, be certain that food is kept high, preferably completely wrapped in plastic and hung between two trees. Trash and food containers that will burn should be placed in the fire at the end of the meal. Other refuse should be packed up and carted out to the trailhead when you're finished camping.

Another precaution is never to sleep in the clothes that you used for cooking. Also, avoid the use of greasy and odorous foods that can reach the nostrils of bears some distance away.

You might also consider the safety precaution of sleeping some distance away from the cooking and food area. All of these minor precautions could prevent you from having a confrontation with a bear—especially at night. If you're fishing in a National Park and do have an incident with a bear, the National Park Service asks that you report it to the rangers.

It goes without saying that if you happen to be wading a stream and a bear suddenly appears, a safe procedure is to slowly work toward the other shore. Should you have trout in a creel, the bear might have smelled them, and you may have to sacrifice the trout if the bear becomes aggressive.

Bears aren't the only big-game animal that can cause problems. Moose can be another threat, particularly during September when the rutting season is in progress. A moose doesn't have the arms or teeth of a bear, but it does have antlers and great bulk plus hoofs, and it is surprisingly fleet-footed. Avoiding one can be done by climbing a tree or at least getting behind one. As a basic rule, never crowd a moose (or any other animal); you never know what experience that particular animal has had with man. Cases of moose attacking people are fairly common. Their eyesight is poor, but they do have a keen sense of smell. Exercise extra caution if you meet a female moose with a calf. She can be extremely aggressive at this time.

You may not live in a part of the country where bears or moose are a real threat, but any fisherman working the pasture lands of a farm may encounter a bull. Bulls are also totally unpredictable and they are unbelievably fast both on a straight course and in swerving. To be safe, walk around a field that contains a bull. If you have to cross it, by all means stay as close to the edge as you possibly can. A bull may ignore you completely—and then again, he may choose to attack.

If you can make it to the fence, get over it anyway you can, even if you have to dive over or through barbed wire. In this case, don't worry about tearing your clothing. Since bulls are attracted by bright colors, remove any bright clothing. This is a good policy even before you enter the field. However, if the bull is charging, fling a garment in his path and hope that the jacket or shirt will distract him temporarily, giving you more time to escape. You can repeat this procedure, stripping as you run. Often, the bull will stop to investigate each item and you'll gain precious seconds.

Approaching a Stream or Lake

Let's take our minds off wildlife for awhile and go fishing. You've arrived at the lake or stream and are ready to approach the spot where you'll begin your fishing. For some reason, most anglers walk right up to the edge of a lake or stream to "look things over." Most gamefish seek shelter and food close to shore. When you stand tall at the water's edge a fish can easily see you and will move off quickly.

But spooking fish is a secondary consideration. A very real danger exists along shorelines in the form of undercut banks. Frequently, the water carves the earth beneath the bank and there is little support left for the weight of the average adult. One second you're standing there fishing, and the next, you're swimming.

Sometimes, it's easy to recognize when a bank has been undercut. In a fast-moving stream, for example, you can bet a bank is somewhat undercut if a strong current swings against that bank before turning. Avoid taking chances and stay at least a couple feet from the water's edge unless you're sure the ground is firm and will support your weight. If you have doubts and still have to traverse the area, do it by keeping your weight on the back foot and probing with the other foot. Then, gradually and carefully shift your weight, staying alert to any loosening of the dirt or feeling of ground giving way under you.

Walking on top of an undercut bank is a dangerous practice. In this instance, the bank gave way and the angler's foot twisted through the soil.

3

WADING

An angler wades a stream or lake to get within casting distance of fish. If he can accomplish this objective as effectively from the bank, there's no reason for him to enter the water.

To be effective, wading must be done carefully, creating a minimum of noise and disturbance. Random plowing through the water can only result in sending every fish into the next county. The same holds true if you persist in kicking loose stones or grinding gravel beneath your feet. You have to sneak up on your quarry.

Incorrect wading can not only ruin the fishing; it can be extremely dangerous. If you're lucky, you'll come away soaking wet; and if you're not that fortunate, you could sustain serious injury or drown. Everything starts with the waders or hip boots.

Choosing Your Waders

Anglers have a wide choice in the style of hip boots and waders, not to mention choices of material. Hip boots, as the name implies, cover the hips and fasten to the trousers belt. They are an excellent choice for both youngsters and senior fishermen. In fact, I finally persuaded my own father to give up his waders in favor of boots. He can get into less trouble with boots. He won't be able to reach some spots, to be sure, but I'm more concerned about his safety. Since no one enjoys getting wet (especially in a cold trout stream) he'll seldom venture close to the boot tops. Because youngsters have a propensity for exploring, hip boots will contain them to some degree. This is particularly important in a fast-moving stream.

Waders are like a pair of rubberized overalls, with some styles reaching only to the waist, while others extend to the armpits. As a rule of thumb, the higher waders reach on an angler,

Hip boots will help to keep youngsters and senior anglers from wading out too deep, while waders enable the fisherman to reach the deeper spots. Note the difference in soles. The felt soles on the waders grip better on slippery, rocky bottoms, while the regular soles on the hip boot are better for muddy bottoms. Wading sandles (foreground) can be slipped over the regular soles to convert them to felt shoes. A repair kit is an essential item on any trip.

If you can place one foot on a chair comfortably and the waders aren't pulling, you've found the correct fit. Too many loose folds of material are just as bad as too tight a fit. Note that the angler has a belt around the middle of the waders to prevent water from pouring in if he slips.

the deeper you can expect him to wade. Don't ask why—it just happens that way.

Waders come in bootfoot models in which the boot is actually part of the wader. They also are available with stocking feet over which two pairs of socks are worn and then a wading shoe or sneaker. Most freshwater streams are paved with rocks that often are extremely slippery. For this reason, the majority of fresh-water anglers prefer waders or wading shoes with thick felt soles. Felt holds on rocks much better than does rubber. Some anglers wear creepers—metal overshoes fitted with spikes or cleats—but these find more favor in salt water.

In selecting boots or waders, the fit is important. Converse-Hodgman, a leading manufacturer of boots and waders, suggests that you be able to place one foot on a chair comfortably while the other wader foot is on the ground. This will make it easy to step on or off a rock or climb a bank. On the other hand, a wader leg that is too long will eventually wear out and perhaps chafe by rubbing on the inside of the legs. If you're going to wade in very cold water, you might want to buy waders with the bootfoot an extra size larger than normal. You can then wear an extra pair of heavy socks without feeling pinched in the toes.

For safety, you should always wear a belt around the middle of the waders, cinched fairly tight. If you should slip, the belt will prevent water from pouring in the top of the waders. Some waders have loops for a belt, but it really doesn't matter. Just carry an old belt with you and secure it around your waist over the waders.

Let's Go Wading

All right, we've chosen the correct waders, cinched a belt around the middle, and we're ready to go fishing. The first step is to climb down the bank and enter the water. By this time, you're well aware of the conditions under which you will be wading. Lakes are one thing and fast-moving streams quite another. For purposes of discussion, let's talk about those fast-moving trout streams since all of the problems exist in them. Then, if you wade slower-moving waters or lakes, you can apply those portions of the technique that fit the situation.

Getting in. Try to enter the water as quietly as possible and as safely as we can. After hiking in and getting ready, it would be a shame to

Whenever possible, enter the stream where the current is slow and there aren't any high banks. This rocky eddy is an ideal spot for easy entry.

spoil the day by getting wet. Take a moment to survey the water in front of you and up and down stream. You're looking for a spot that is relatively shallow, out of the main current, with a low bank or a gently sloping one. The idea is to get into the water as easily as you can. Then you can worry about moving toward the lies where the fish may be.

As you glance along the bank, be particularly aware of root loops on which you could stub a toe or possibly strands of barbed wire from a knocked-down fence that could puncture a boot. If you can locate a gravel bar, you're ahead of the game. Even in shallow water, place one foot in the water first and then, when you have firm footing, bring the other one into the water.

Unfortunately, it's not always that easy and sometimes you have to compromise. The worst situation is where you have to come from a high bank into fast and deep water. This is a situation that should be studied carefully before you attempt it. When you are scanning any bank for an entry point, try to pick a spot that does not contain loose dirt or rock that will cause you to slide. Sometimes, that's the only choice you have. If that's the case, and you have to slide, place your feet parallel to the water rather than at right angles. With your feet parallel you won't pitch forward.

The secret of safe wading is to concern yourself with one foot at a time. You've just entered the water and have planted both feet firmly. Place your weight on one foot and slide the other one forward slowly and carefully. Take

Fly fishermen can get into trouble trying to retrieve a fly from the branches of a streamside tree. One of the best ways is to use your rod and line to pull the branch to you. Loop the V formed by the rod tip and line over the branch, then work the rod down until you have the line in both hands and pull the branch to you.

a comfortable step forward with all your weight on the rear foot. Now find a spot for the front foot. Wiggle it around if you have to until it's secure. Transfer your weight to the front foot and slide the rear foot up to it. That's the basic step and it's the least likely to get you into trouble. At the same time, you'll be approaching a trout lie quietly.

Trout fishermen find advantages to working upstream while they are fishing. First, trout face upstream, as we mentioned before, and are less aware of an angler approaching from behind. Second, when you hook a trout, it will run downstream, creating a disturbance only in the area you have finished fishing. Third, the best way to work a fly is to cast across and slightly upstream.

If the current is extremely strong, you may have difficulty working upstream since it could prove extremely fatiguing. If so, you'll just have to select pools and try to work them. If you have to cross the stream, you are better off wading across the current on a slight downstream diagonal. Try it directly downstream and you stand a good chance of stubbing your toe and pitching forward, or being swept off your feet.

The depth of the water in which you wade is also important. It's sometimes safer and easier to wade in waist-deep water than knee-deep water. When the water hits you at knee level, it can more easily knock you down.

Then there's the problem of holes. Step in one and you could be over the top of the waders. The sliding method of wading will prevent this, because if you can't feel bottom at a comfortable depth, you can always back up on the solid foot and try a different course.

When you learn the hydrodynamics of a stream, you'll begin to realize that you can often avoid the main current by seeking protection behind rocks. It's possible to think out a wading route that will force you to cross open current only a few times.

Sometimes, the bottom will be soft and you'll feel yourself sinking into it. This can easily throw you off balance. Lifting a foot will be difficult, and you'll frequently find it's easier to try to twist or wriggle a foot free. Weeds can present a similar problem of entanglement; you should exercise caution when moving between weeds or lily pads. Also, make sure there's a solid foundation under any islands you spot before you climb out of the water. One of them could surprise you and be nothing more than floating plants.

Secure footing is the key to wading and it's also an important consideration when you stand still while fishing. It is not advisable to stand with both feet parallel and your back to the current. Instead, plant the downstream foot firmly and keep the rear foot slightly to the side. When possible, and especially in a strong current, it's safer to stand with your side toward the current than to take the brunt of the force on your front or back. Your side will offer less resistance.

Wading out never seems to be a problem, but suddenly you want to turn around—and realize that you may not be able to do it. Remember that the current is only hitting your side if you're moving across the stream. When you turn, it's going to pour on you with full force against a broader target area. The *only* way to turn is into the current. If you turn away from it, you may be swept off your feet.

Execute the turn by slowly sliding the upstream foot in the direction of the turn. Keep the downstream foot planted firmly and lean into the current for balance if you have to. When the upstream foot is planted again, place your weight on it and slide the downstream foot around until it is behind (still downstream) and to the side. Plant it firmly, shift your weight again, and repeat the procedure.

> Turning broadside to the current with your back facing upstream is a dangerous practice—especially in knee-deep water. The force of the current can easily sweep you off your feet.

In an emergency, you can often regain your balance by pushing your fishing rod under water. You won't damage the rod, and it will act as a stabilizing influence.

Wading staff. You can use your fishing rod as a point of balance by pushing it under the water. The direction of the push depends on the way you are falling, but the rod will frequently save the day. However, a better method in fast water is to carry a wading staff. Wading staffs are available at tackle shops. Some are adjustable in length; others are fixed. If you go skiing or know a skier, you can make an excellent one from an old ski pole. A wading staff should be lightweight, and you should

In fast water or where there are slippery rocks, a wading staff is the best friend you have. The proper technique is to place the staff ahead of you and upstream. It should always be used as a third leg on the upstream side. Note how swiftness of the current has pushed the landing net away from angler's side.

have it tied to your fishing vest or waders with a length of light line. That way, you can drop it when it's not needed and the current will keep it out of the way. If the water looks treacherous and you don't have a wading staff, you can make one from a stout stick.

The wading staff is like a third leg, and it helps tremendously in crossing fast water. With the staff held on your upstream side, the technique is to plant the staff first, then move the upstream foot, and finally the downstream foot.

Crossing a fast-moving stream or river requires as much mental exercise as physical. Using a wading staff to probe for a pocket behind the big rock, Bob Steenson works his way behind this natural protection where the current will be reduced.

Getting out of the stream on a log can be a dangerous operation. You may lose your balance and fall or the log may break under your weight.

In climbing out of the water, follow a procedure similar to the one you used in entering the water. Look for the same type of easy egress route with relatively calm water and a low bank. If you have a wading staff, use it to help you keep your balance while you climb out of the water. Unless you can leave the water easily and comfortably, place your rod on the bank along with creel, net, and other paraphrenalia, freeing your hands and eliminating items that may snag on a streamside bush or tree.

If the bank is high, look for a handhold and a spot where you will have room to place your feet. Selecting a handhold is critical. Test it first before putting all of your weight on it. Often, a vine or trunk of a small tree will do the job. In deeper water, you can often find a ledge to sit on. Perhaps it's easier to sit on the bank than to climb out. Then you can take your time in negotiating the sloping portion of the bank.

Suppose You Fall In

Sooner or later in your fishing career, you can expect to get wet while wading. One of the wader legs might spring a leak, but more than likely you'll step in a hole and go over the tops of your waders. The belt around the waist that we talked about earlier will prevent water from pouring in and probably reduce it to a cold and uncomfortable trickle.

There was a time when anglers believed they were goners if they had an accident in a pair of waders. This has been disproved so many times that there's little doubt you will survive no matter what the conditions. In still water, you need only reverse direction and walk back to a shallower depth. You may have to take a swimming stroke or two to aid you, but there's not much problem. And, if you must, you can also remove the waders in the water and use them as a buoyant life preserver by forcing the waistband underwater and trapping air inside.

Banish the old concern about air being trapped in your waders and forcing your feet over your head. Those who have tested this theory discovered that, if anything, you will float like a log on the surface. That means that you can roll over on your back and paddle your way to safety.

Most accidents with waders occur in a fast-moving stream when the angler is swept off his feet or loses his balance and pitches forward. Perhaps the cause is stepping in a deep hole. Regardless of the reason, there are several things you can do. The first is to remain calm and recognize that this is only a minor inconvenience. Make the stream or river work for you and save your energy. Your course is going to be downstream, so go with the current. If the water isn't over your head, try to take big steps on your tiptoes, bouncing up and down as the current carries you downstream.

Keep a plan firmly in mind. You're going downstream and you're going to work toward shore. If you know the river or stream you might be aware that there is a shallow bar below the pool and the current will carry you there. Your course should be toward shore. Sometimes the water will be far too deep for you to touch bottom. When that happens, use your arms to swim. You won't be able to use your legs effectively with heavy waders, so conserve your energy and just use your arms. Remember that the current will be carrying you, so all you have to do is make a little progress toward shore.

If the current is particularly strong and your course will take you near the bank or an island (and there are no shallow spots or eddies where you can stand) make a grab for anything that will stop you. You might be able to hold on to an overhanging branch, a rock, roots, small trees, stop your progress and be able to pull yourself ashore.

Some anglers are currently using inflatable fly-fishing vests or simply carrying a small CO_2 life-preserver packet attached to their wader straps. If an accident occurs, they merely inflate the vest or squeeze the packet and float on the life preserver.

In the extremely cold water of many northern trout and salmon streams, you won't have an excessive amount of time to reach shore before the numbing effects of the water begin to sap your strength. In this situation, don't shed any clothing since it will serve as insulation even though it is wet. Instead, concentrate on getting to shore as quickly as you can or at least reaching the shallows where you can walk out with little effort.

Learning to read water will help in these situations, for you can often get an idea of the depth and bottom by looking at the surface. Riffles are generally shallow, and you know that rapids have plenty of rocks. If you're going to be carried through wild rapids, try to get your feet going downstream first to protect your head and chest from the rocks. Naturally, all of these recommendations are based on the ideal; it is more than likely that the average angler will do his best to scramble to safety any way he can. However, I hope these suggestions will help him to make the right moves.

4

FISHING FROM BOATS

To the average angler, a boat merely serves as transportation to the fishing grounds and as a platform for casting. It is precisely because of the fact that the fishermen is intent on catching fish that he often violates the rules of boating safety.

Safety dictates that you take several steps before leaving the dock, and then separate fishing and boating into equally important facets of the trip. Anglers set out in every imaginable type of boat from a canoe to an outboard skiff. Each has its own characteristics and each body of water has its pitfalls. The successful fisherman is frequently a competent boat handler. He has to be if he wants to get the most from his fishing trips.

Before You Leave the Dock

Water is not the place for taking chances. National statistics sober us quickly and point out tragedies by the score that could have been averted. Start with the belief that no fish is worth risking human life.

If you're going to fish from your own boat, you should know how to operate it. More important, you should be thoroughly familiar with its particular characteristics and understand precisely what you can and cannot do with it. Each boat is a compromise at best. Even the largest seagoing yachts are a compromise between comfort and seaworthiness. As long as you are willing to respect the limitations of your craft, you shouldn't encounter difficulty. The problem occurs when you decide to test those limitations.

With a rental boat, the problems can be magnified, because you are seldom familiar with all of its characteristics and few sportsmen take the time to insure that it is properly equipped.

Before you leave the dock, you're going to be busy. The first step is to check off each item of safety equipment aboard the boat, whether the boat is yours or is rented.

Start with life jackets or life cushions. There must be one for every passenger on board. Youngsters should be dressed in life jackets from the moment they enter the docking area, and these should not be removed until they are back in the car for the trip home. Life jackets should be stowed on board where they can be reached easily. Too often they wind up buried in a locker and cannot be reached in time to avert tragedy.

Anchor. This item is of course particularly important on a large lake where you could be blown a great distance from shore. There are many types of anchors available and you should insist on the type that will work in the water you are fishing. In very deep water, when fishing from a small boat, you can rig up an emergency setup that could save the day.

Youngsters must always wear an approved life jacket whenever they are around water. Even if they can swim, a life jacket is a worthwhile precaution against tragedy.

Fishermen in small boats seldom carry enough anchor line to reach bottom if they happen to get in trouble in deep water. A spool of heavy monofilament fishing line and a lead-weighted gang hook makes a perfect emergency anchor and takes up little room on board.

Since most boat liveries or even private owners only use a set amount of anchor line, situations could be encountered where the anchor won't reach bottom. Fishermen have licked this problem by fashioning an emergency anchor out of a weighted treble hook and a long length of 100-pound-test monofilament fishing line. The line and treble hook take up very little room and you can carry several hundred feet of line with little inconvenience. Should you drift out in deep water and have no means of propulsion, this anchor will hold you in one spot.

Check gas. If the boat is outboard powered, you should check the gas on board and make sure you have more than enough for a day's fishing. It is surprising how easily you can miscalculate and run out of gas. For example, a boat might burn two gallons of gas an hour, providing it's up on plane. Yet, you could encounter choppy weather and be forced to poke along just under plane, using at least twice the fuel you normally would.

Carry spare hose and pins. The hoses connecting portable gas tanks to the motor have a habit of breaking down periodically. Possibly, somebody steps on one and ruptures it, or a fitting becomes defective and leaks air. That's why it's always a good idea to carry a spare hose with you, especially if you're in a remote region or planning to cross a big body of water. If the motor's propeller is attached with a cotter pin, be sure to carry spare pins. In fact, if the boat is your own, carry an extra propeller in case you bend one on a log or rock.

Chart and compass. Unless you're going to fish a small body of water that you know thoroughly, you should have a chart and a compass on board. Even if you rent the boat, you can carry your own chart. It is amazing how different things can look in fog or haze. The compass and chart can keep you on course if the visibility becomes bad.

Boats sometimes leak, so you should make certain there is a can or ladle for bailing on board. If you're launching your own boat, don't forget to check if the transom plug is tight before you slide the boat into the water.

Water. Even though you're planning a short trip without taking food along, you should always carry a container of fresh water. Remember that in an emergency you can go for days without eating, but water is vital, particularly in a warm climate.

Tackle stowage is important to consider, from the standpoint of both personal safety and rod care. On your own boat, providing adequate tackle stowage is no problem, but on a rental boat it is. Tackleboxes should be placed out of the way so that they are not underfoot every time someone tries to move around the boat. In a small boat, each angler should fish from a designated area and his gear should be close to him so he doesn't have to disturb his partner every time he wants to change a lure. Fish are particularly sensitive to sound that is transmitted through the hull, so every effort should be made to avoid dragging a tacklebox across the deck. This is very important in aluminum boats where every sound is magnified many times. You'll find that an old towel or rag under the tacklebox can eliminate the transmission of sound.

Rods should be stowed as far out of the way as practical, with hooks securely fastened on the inside. Otherwise you run the risk of brushing against a hook and catching it in a trouser leg. Keep in mind that very few rods break under pressure. Most are victims of carelessness and are crunched in car doors, trunk lids, or boats. Impact is another enemy of the modern glass fishing rod. When rods bounce on a seat or against the gunwale, they can sustain hairline fractures in the glass. Under fishing pressure, the rod splits in two.

If you break a hollow glass rod under pressure, it will actually explode into three to five pieces. When the rod breaks in one spot, you can be sure that something weakened the rod—often the pounding it took while the boat was in motion. A rag tied around the rods at the point where they rest against a seat or other edge will cushion the blows. A piece of indoor-outdoor carpeting can also serve the same purpose.

Before you go fishing, there are one or two other chores you should accomplish. Perhaps the worst disasters occur when a boat is overloaded or overpowered. Check the capacity of the boat you are about to use and make sure it can safely carry the number of passengers and gear that you plan to take along. Otherwise, use two boats. There should be plenty of freeboard between the water and the gunwales. Using too powerful an outboard is another violation. You'll find a rating plate fastened to the transom of the boat telling you the maximum power the boat can handle and the total weight that may be loaded. If the plate isn't there, ask someone at the dock.

Finally, if you don't know the lake or river well, ask about pitfalls to avoid. A few minutes conversation can tell you about hidden bars, submerged rocks, and other dangers that lurk in every body of water. Your informant can also give you information about the best fishing locations and how to approach them.

Attaching the motor. Every year, hundreds of outboard motors are fished off the bottom. They were dropped while the owners were trying to fasten them to the transom. In attaching a motor, lay it out on the dock first, opening the clamps to accommodate the transom width. Then, get in the boat. Have someone pass the motor to you or lift it off the dock and set the motor in the boat. When you are well-balanced, lift the motor to the transom and mount it. Trying to climb aboard with a heavy outboard in hand is courting disaster. A water bath seldom helps an outboard— even if you can recover it.

Shoving off. When you've checked the boat thoroughly and gathered information about the water, you're ready to shove off. Load your passengers carefully and keep the load as close to the centerline of the boat as possible. Only one person should board at a time, and he should *step* into the boat rather than jump in. When the second person is ready to come aboard, he should announce his intentions and do so when everyone is braced for the sudden shifting that will take place. Too often, the first man aboard is busy doing something and when the second man climbs in, the boat lurches, the first man reacts and both people wind up in the water.

On the Water

After releasing the docking lines, always start off slowly. If you're rowing, one or two strokes will usually clear the docking area. Should there be a chance of bumping another boat, station your fishing partner where he can fend off.

With an outboard, you are legally and morally responsible for the wake the boat creates. Respect the property of others and taxi away from the docking area slowly. If you're in tight quarters, don't hesitate to push out by hand or use an oar or paddle. Then, when you are clear, throw the motor in gear and move away from the dock. If you have your own boat and are taking the docking lines with you, they should be secured and stowed immediately. The object is to keep the cockpit clear at all times.

How fast you proceed to the fishing area depends on a number of things. You should consider the water conditions, the load you are carrying, the type of boat, and the power you can generate. It is seldom wise to run at full throttle when three-quarter throttle is far more economical. Avoid any sudden turns and try to remember to warn your passengers of any maneuvers you contemplate. It goes without saying that passengers should be seated while you are running.

Fishing from a small boat requires teamwork. The movements of one angler can easily throw the other angler off balance and either or both can fall overboard in the confusion. You can prevent this by moving slowly and deliberately, avoiding sudden movements. Invariably, a fisherman who is casting likes to stand up in the boat. For some reason, nobody can cast sitting down unless he is forced to do it that way. Whether or not anglers stand depends on the water conditions and the type of boat. If there's any question, you might want to take turns standing or both of you remain seated. If you do stand, find a comfortable position and then refrain from shifting without warning.

Weather

Every fisherman is almost forced to become an amateur meteorologist. Nowhere is it more important than when the angler pursues his sport from a small boat. He simply has to be able to recognize nature's weather signals and react to them. Before starting out, a small boatman should have an idea of the local forecast and what to expect during the day on the water. Yet, forecasters are known to be wrong, and it is only through an understanding of weather systems that the fisherman can avoid discomfort, if not disaster.

The longer you are in the outdoors, the greater the respect you will have for the elements. That doesn't mean that you have to fear them, but you should harbor a healthy respect for the force they can generate. The object is not to take chances. If you've ever seen a wave twist steel like it was baling wire, you'll never forget the sight.

When the signs indicate that heavy weather is approaching, you should already be on your way in. That's not the time to work for just one more fish. When common sense tells you to go home, follow your instinct and leave the fishing for another day. Very often, you can be in a safe harbor or almost to the dock when the weather finally hits. If you've made a mistake and the weather isn't as severe as you predicted, nothing is lost. You did the right thing; next time it may save your boat, equipment, and even your life.

Frequently, however, weather strikes before you can get back to shore. By the time you are aware of the change, it's too late to do much about it. Remember from the start that there's no law that says you must get back to the dock and there's no time limit when you must be back. Your safety is of paramount importance and the steps you take should be directed toward this goal. Of course, a great deal depends on how bad the weather really is (or promises to get) and the boat you are using. If you are rowing and are a good distance from the dock when the wind comes up, you might not be able to make it back.

Perhaps you're in an outboard skiff; the lake becomes extremely rough and you start to take water over the bow. Possibly, you've never seen conditions so bad. What then? An experienced seaman is both patient and calm in the face of tough going. Above all, he's never in a hurry. If your boat will float under calm conditions, it will float under rough conditions. The object now is to keep the boat afloat and minimize any risk to you and your passengers.

If you can slowly and carefully work your way back to the dock, go ahead and try it. Don't be in a hurry; the dock isn't going anywhere. Use only as much speed and power as you need without risking the chance of burying the bow in a following sea (the waves are going in the same direction you are). Keep all of the weight in the boat low and near the centerline. You might want to instruct your passengers to sit on the deck. If the bow is too low, move some of the weight back toward you. If you have to, don't hesitate to jettison extra weight.

There are times when you can't make it back to the dock, and trying is pure folly. In most cases, you'll find it better to barely maintain headway into the seas, regardless of the direction from which they are coming, and wait out the storm. Just point the bow into the waves or on a quartering angle across the waves and maintain the power needed to keep the bow there. You can do the same thing if you are rowing.

Supposing you run out of gas or the motor won't work or the oarsman is exhausted. Then what? Try to avoid taking the waves broadside. If you toss and pitch at the mercy of the seas, you're in for dangerous and heavy rolls. All of this can be averted by rigging a sea anchor. Don't confuse a sea anchor with that heavy piece of hardware you carry to hold the boat

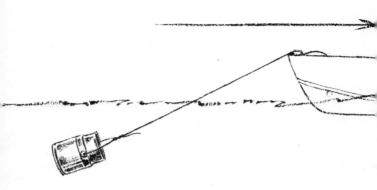

in one place. A sea anchor (or drogue, as it is called) is usually a canvas bag or bucket with a hole in the bottom to let water pass through. You can fashion one out of anything at hand. That minnow bucket you carry is ideal. How about the tin can you brought along for bailing?

Make a jury rig and tie either the anchor line to it or that length of heavy monofilament you brought along for emergencies. Stream the sea anchor off the bow a distance of several feet. You'll have to adjust the distance to suit the conditions. Tie the line to the bow cleat or make it secure so that it rides directly over the bow. That sea anchor will now hold the bow into the wind as you drift. It could save your life.

By the way, if you have jacket-type life preservers on board, put them on at the first sign of bad weather and leave them on. Only an inexperienced boatman considers himself above

When all power fails, a sea anchor will keep a drifting boat's bow into the wind and prevent taking the waves broadside. Tie the line to a bow cleat and let the sea anchor drift off the bow.

such a precaution. The veteran won't hesitate to don a life jacket or keep his hand on a life-preserver cushion. In rough weather, clear the decks of every item that can shift or move, securing the gear the best way possible.

Anchoring

You might want to stillfish, or perhaps you've decided to hold in one spot by dropping the anchor. Anchors are simple to handle, yet they invariably lead to more trouble than any other item of equipment. If you're going to anchor on a rocky bottom, the anchor should be fitted with a length of chain before you attach the anchor line. This helps to prevent abrasion.

When you're ready to anchor, follow a basic procedure. Tie the end of the anchor line to the bow cleat so you won't lose the anchor if the boat is swept away swiftly. Then, make certain the anchor line is coiled neatly, enabling it to flow out as the boat drifts back from its mooring. Take out any knots in the line and insure that it is not lying around the deck where it can twist around someone's ankle or destroy some equipment as it pays out.

If there's any current running (or wind), you know that the boat is going to drift before the anchor holds. Therefore, move ahead of the spot where you want the boat to rest and *lower the anchor* over the side. Anchors should never be thrown. Let the anchor line pay out freely before you even think of taking a strain. Guide

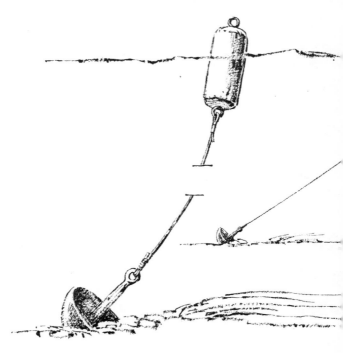

it through your hands. When you have four to six times the amount of line out as the depth of the water, secure the anchor line to the bow cleat and it should hold. On spotty bottoms, you may have to try the procedure over again before getting the anchor to grab.

Another trick worth remembering is the use of an anchor buoy. You can attach a cork float to the anchor line and then clip to the float with your bow line. There are several quick release setups that can be employed. If you hook a good fish and want to follow your quarry downstream, you need only uncouple the line from the float.

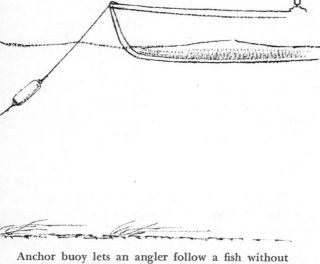

Anchor buoy lets an angler follow a fish without having to haul up the anchor. Attach a cork float to the anchor line, then clip to the float with the bow line. Release the bow line when you want to move. The anchor stays in place.

The boat is free to move and the anchor will stay in place, marked by the float. A seat cushion, by the way, can accomplish the same thing. You'll also find that if the current is too strong to pull the anchor or you can't run up on it comfortably, you can mark the anchor and line by tying a cushion to the end of the anchor line.

On a rowboat or skiff, the anchor line should always be attached to the bow cleat and not the transom if there is any kind of current running. Should you attach the anchor line to the stern of the boat, you might discover that the force of the water against the boat will pull the stern under or at least lower it enough for water to enter. The same thing goes for a canoe, even though canoes have high bows and sterns. A friend of mine took a fishing trip on a major river and tied the anchor line to the thwart in the canoe. It didn't take long for the current to upset the canoe, and the anglers lost all of their fishing tackle.

Pulling in an anchor is another simple operation if it is done right. Pressure and not speed moves the boat over the spot where the anchor is in contact with the bottom. Leave the anchor line attached to the bow cleat. Start pulling on it steadily, holding tightly between pulls. If you have an outboard, you can run up on the anchor slowly, but be careful that the anchor line does not work under the boat and foul the propeller.

Eventually, the anchor line will reach the position of short stay. This is the point where one more pull should free the anchor. On some bottoms, it will come out easily; on others, the job is tough. You can save your back and shoulder muscles by letting the boat work for you. When you can't pull and gain anymore line, hold the line securely against the gunwale of the boat at the bow. You'll find that the bobbing motion of the boat should break the anchor's hold. Then, pull the anchor carefully, but steadily, until it is alongside the boat.

Care must be exercised in pulling the anchor the final few feet. More than one angler has hauled away quickly, only to bury the flukes in the bottom of the boat. Instead, look for the anchor and lift it abroad. If it's covered with mud or weeds, shake them loose in the water by swishing the anchor around before lifting it aboard. When the anchor is aboard, stow it immediately and clear the decks.

If you anchored in rocks, it might not be a simple procedure to get the anchor out. You may have to run the boat around to the up-current side and maneuver until the anchor comes free. The only solution to this problem is to try different angles of pull until it comes loose. Of course, there are certain types of anchors that are better for rocky bottoms and many of these have quick-release mechanisms built in. If you regularly anchor over this type of bottom, you may want to purchase one.

Falling Overboard

If you fall overboard, you may only get wet and have a humorous story to relate when you get back to the dock. However, the shock of entering cold water without warning can have a pronounced effect on an individual, particularly on an older person. Just the slap of your body against the surface of the water can stun you. The logbooks are filled with stories of people who fell overboard, surfaced, appeared to be all right, and then disappeared forever.

It's not always easy to do, but if you know you're going overboard, your first concern is to fall or jump clear of the boat. There are times when it is far better to get wet than to try to stop your fall and hit your head on the gunwale. The instant someone falls overboard, all hands should immediately swing into action. Toss a line, life preserver, or both to the victim before maneuvering the boat.

If the boat is moving at the time of the accident, turn the bow in the direction that the victim fell overboard, thereby moving the stern away from him so that he will not hit the boat or get chopped up by the propeller. Then, of course, stop the boat and pick him up. It's always a good idea to rehearse in your mind just what you would do if this type of accident occurred. Then, if it does happen, you can react automatically without having to think.

Care should be taken in helping the victim back abroad. If everybody jams one gunwale trying to lift the man aboard, you run the risk of pushing that gunwale under water and swamping the boat. Sometimes, in small boats, you'll have to shift your weight to one side while the angler climbs back in on the other. It goes without saying that if the victim appears to be injured, you might have to send someone else into the water to assist him. Of course, if there are only the two of you in the boat, it can be tricky business, and your best plan is to stay in the boat and get the boat to him—unless he disappears under water.

If it is difficult to get the victim into the boat without capsizing, and the shore isn't too far away, you may be able to tow him to shore if he isn't injured and is in good enough physical condition to withstand the strain. In cold water, however, you must get the victim out as soon as you possibly can.

The worst tragedies occur when a boat capsizes. There can be mass confusion when men and equipment are tossed into the water. The first man to surface should try to make certain that everyone has been thrown clear of the boat. If the life cushions were on the seats, they are probably floating nearby. Get to them as quickly as possible and then use them to reach the boat. An overturned boat will not sink, and if you can swim to the boat and hold on, it's your best chance for survival. No matter how short the distance, don't try to swim to shore. Rather, hold on to the boat, and by kicking, you may be able to work it into shore.

There is only one time when you must abandon the boat and try to reach shore. That is when the water is icy and you know that you cannot survive the cold. Even in icy water, you may be able to pull yourself up on the overturned boat and get out of the water.

No matter how long you have to cling to the boat (if the weather is warm enough), stay with it. It's far easier to spot an overturned boat than it is to see a man in the water. In some cases, you may be able to get back in the boat even though it is filled with water. But even if you can't reboard, don't leave the boat. That "short swim" to shore has proved fatal to too many fishermen. Above all, keep your wits about you. It's not easy to stay calm, but it will invariably lead to the best solution for the circumstances.

Canoes

Canoes are notoriously tippy, but they make excellent fishing platforms in some waters. Experts claim that a canoe is stable if handled by skilled paddlers. Most of the safety precautions outlined for rowboats and skiffs apply equally to canoes. However, there are a few additional points worth mentioning.

When stepping aboard, place one hand on each gunwale (side) of the canoe and then step as close to the centerline as possible. By placing your hands on the gunwales, you distribute the weight and keep the canoe fairly stable. Another way of doing this is to lay your paddle across the gunwales and hold the paddle at the point where it touches the sides. Once on board, move to your position and get comfortable.

If it was important to avoid sudden movements in a small boat, it's doubly important in a canoe. Deliberation is the watchword. Move slowly and let your partner know what you are doing so he can be prepared. The cardinal rule of fishing from a canoe is that you *never* stand. All fishing is done from a sitting or kneeling position. If the canoe should overturn, hold on

Getting into a canoe can be a safe operation if you do it properly. The paddle should be placed across the gunwales to steady the canoe and your hands should press at the points where the paddle crosses the gunwales. Step in slowly near the center of the canoe.

to the gunwale and use your legs to kick and propel it toward shore.

In situations where a canoe could easily tip over, veterans pack all of their gear in waterproof containers and then lash these to the thwarts or gunwales. If you're on an extended trip, pack the gear in sequence so that the items you will need first or those utensils for a shore lunch are readily available.

Towing a canoe correctly and safely requires a bridle under the bow to which the towing line is attached. Otherwise, the bow will "dig in" when the canoe is towed and it will swamp or overturn.

If for some reason you find it necessary to tow a canoe behind another boat or have someone tow you while in the canoe, a simple line from the bow of the canoe to the towing boat will not do the job. You'll discover that the canoe will dart wildly from side to side. Instead, make a bridle by looping the line under the bow of the canoe and bringing one end up on either side. With a bridle, you can tow a canoe easily as long as you keep the bow high and out of water.

One of the rules of paddling a canoe is to keep your body rigid from the waist down. The man in the bow sets the pace and the man in the stern follows the rhythm. Be sure to change sides frequently so you won't tire. Paddle at a steady but comfortable pace, otherwise you will soon be exhausted. Use a simple, clean stroke, repeating it over and over with a definite rhythm.

Above all, unless you are extremely experienced, don't take a chance trying to negotiate rapids. That's the time to head for shore and either lead the canoe through calm water along the bank by a bow rope and stern rope, or portage it around the obstructions. It might take a few extra minutes to pack the canoe for portage, but it's worth every single second.

And finally, if you do decide to swap positions in the canoe, don't try it in midstream. Paddle ashore, get out, and then climb back aboard in reverse order.

5

WILDERNESS FISHING

In this age of jet aircraft, helicopters, all-terrain vehicles, and fast boats, it's possible to fish almost any region of the world. In fact, the emphasis in recent years has been on wilderness fishing, and sportsmen have been prompted to test areas that they never would have dreamed of visiting a few years ago. It's been said that you can reach any waters of the world in twenty-four hours. On the other hand, you might prefer a slow-moving packtrain that carries you to a mountain lake loaded with trout that have yet to see an angler.

All of the safety advice given so far will apply no matter where you fish. Yet, if your purpose is to explore the wilderness—and all of us harbor that urge—there are a few additional precautions you should take.

First of all, it's doubtful that you will be the first person in the world to reach a particular lake or stream. Take the time to do a little research and track down people who have already been there. It's surprising how much you can learn by letter or long-distance phone call. All of this information will help you pack the right gear and be prepared for the fishing you plan to encounter.

Before you leave, visit your family physician for a complete physical checkup. This is essential if you're approaching the age of a senior fisherman. Tell the doctor of your plans and the type of trip you have planned. He'll probably wish you well and ask that you let him know about the fishing when you get back. But if he does uncover something serious, he can warn you about going and you won't have to worry about being in the bush country when a medical emergency strikes. You're far better off postponing the trip and having the problem taken care of where there are adequate medical facilities.

Altitude

Anyone who reads the sport pages in the newspaper is well aware of the training that athletes undergo before participating in events held in high altitudes. Before going to Mexico City for the Olympics, athletes trained for months at correspondingly high altitudes where the air was thinner so that their bodies could get acclimated. Yet many a sportsman leaves his office (after months of a sedentary life), flies to a base camp at a high altitude, and sets forth on a hike to a choice fishing spot. He has suddenly increased his rate of physical activity, and in high country where the oxygen supply is low. The result is often extreme fatigue, or worse, a form of mountain sickness.

The symptoms of mountain sickness are weakness, headache, nausea, diarrhea, and dizziness. It comes from overexertion at high altitudes, and people who are not in prime physical condition are among its victims. There is also a more dangerous type that could easily cause death if not treated. Also caused by overexertion at high altitudes, it is characterized by involuntary spasms of the blood vessels, forcing fluids into the air chambers in the lungs.

Several weeks before you leave on a wilderness trip, start a routine of exercises. Build your body to a level where it can tolerate more than the normal exercise you might get from walking around the office. An excellent way to accomplish this if you live in a town with a big stadium is to walk (and later run) up the stadium steps from the field to the top row. Be sure to wear your field shoes or boots.

When you arrive at the base camp, remember to take it easy. Don't rush out and try to accomplish everything at once. Instead, pace yourself and rest frequently. Do a little more each day, but don't push yourself. It won't take long to become acclimated, and then you'll be able to do everything with relative ease.

Motion Sickness

Travel means transportation and the risk of motion sickness. It doesn't affect everyone, but some people get sick in anything from an elevator to a jet plane. Today, there are a host of drugs on the market that help to prevent motion sickness, and they can be purchased at any drug counter. If there's any doubt that you might contract motion sickness, don't hesitate to take the pills. Your family doctor can recommend the best type for you. Some make you drowsy, but all are effective. In fact, astronauts sometimes take motion sickness pills as a preventive measure.

In addition to the pills, it helps to get a good night's rest before you travel and to eat lightly. Select foods that you know you can digest without difficulty. Don't stuff yourself with a heavy meal just before traveling if you know you are susceptible to motion sickness. You'll also find that dry soda crackers will sometimes help to settle your stomach if you start to feel some of the effects of motion sickness. Remember, too, that it's just as bad to leave your stomach completely empty.

Special Medical Kit

Many of the remote regions in the United States and in foreign countries are a great distance from satisfactory medical facilities. Even with helicopters and modern air travel, weather can be a problem. A plane might not be able to get in or get out for several days. My own writing assignments take me to a number of these areas, and with the help of my family physician I have compiled a special medical kit with a number of drugs and medications that the average traveler would not carry. The kit is by no means complete, but it is a start toward a more comprehensive one based on experience.

Let me emphasize that there are two schools of thought about laymen carrying some of these medications. Some doctors feel that more harm than good can be done by the incorrect administration of medications. They reason that it is difficult for the untrained to make a diagnosis. On the other hand, there are those physicians who see no great harm in carrying the drugs. Their argument is that medical advice can sometimes be obtained a lot easier than the correct drugs. Therefore, if you have the drugs with you, you may be able to locate a physician who will tell you which ones to use. There's also the possibility of describing the symptoms over a shortwave radio and having a doctor recommend the medication when you tell him what you have with you.

If you do decide to prepare and carry a special medical kit, do so with your doctor's knowledge and recommendations. Most important, recognize the inherent dangers involved in administering these drugs without full knowledge of the illness or the effects of the drugs. Remember, these drugs are for extreme emergencies; that's why you are carrying the kit.

Start a kit with the basic household medications you would normally buy without a prescription. These would include aspirin (or a related product) for headaches and minor pain, an analgesic alkalizer for simple stomach distress, and any medications you are already taking. In my own kit, I carry a stronger pain medication, broad-based antibiotics, a second antibiotic in case the infection is immune to the first, antihistamine capsules for nasal congestion, pills for bacterial dysentary, medication for diarrhea, medication for constipation, suppositories to stop vomiting if I can't get anything down orally, and a mild tranquilizer. In addition, I pack an antibiotic ointment for skin infections and an ointment for the eyes. Oil of cloves, dental wax, and a dental poultice are

When traveling to a remote region, the author carries a pill case with medications prescribed by his physician to cover a wide range of ailments.

there if I encounter difficulty with my teeth. Included, too, are bandages, gauze pads, first-aid cream or iodine, long stretch-bandages, and a snakebite kit. I am considering adding other items, but I am trying to keep the size and weight down to eliminate packing and traveling problems. Once you start building your kit you'll quickly realize that you can't carry everything. Your goal should be to hedge against those emergencies that are most likely to occur.

If you do carry a medical kit, remember that it is strictly for your own use. You cannot go around playing doctor and prescribe for anyone else in camp who may be ill. Of course, you can make your medications available to a doctor and let him prescribe them for another patient. Otherwise, you're practicing medicine without a license.

As I said earlier, you'll hear arguments both ways. However, for my own well-being I personally believe in carrying the medicines I outlined. This is my decision based on the advice of my doctor. Before you do anything, consult your own doctor and abide by what he advises.

Eyeglasses

If you wear eyeglasses, by all means carry an extra pair or two on any trip to a wilderness area. If you don't wear them all the time, loop a piece of monofilament or flyline around the temple bars and let them hang around your neck so you won't lose them. Above all, don't keep anything of value, *including eyeglasses,* in a top shirt or jacket pocket. When you lean over the water to net a fish, you could lose everything while you're scooping up your catch.

It also pays to carry extra sunglasses with you. Those of us who depend on a good pair of Polaroids to spot fish under the surface treasure our sunglasses. It might sound unusual, but we put them around our necks as soon as we get dressed and seldom remove them until we're ready to turn in at night. Using a fine file, I flatten the back end of the temple bars and then drill a hole from the end of the temple bar to a point on the outside a half-inch away. I thread a length of monofilament through the hole from the back and knot it so it won't pull through.

Then, I push the monofilament through the hole in the other temple bar, adjusting the length so that, with the glasses on, I can get three or four fingers between the back of my head and the monofilament.

You'll find that there are a couple of advantages to this method. One is that the knots will not chafe the side of your face or temple because they are on the outside and resting tightly against the temple bar. Another feature is that when the glasses hang down around your neck, they will be high on the chest. If they were lower, you would run the risk of damaging them more easily.

Water

In the far north country, it's a treat to dip a cup in a virgin lake and drink all the water you want. However, in some parts of the world, you must exercise considerable caution before drinking the water. If there's the slightest doubt in your mind, DON'T DRINK ANY WATER. Some of us carry Halazone tablets to purify water. Follow the directions on the label and after about a half hour you can drink the water.

Tropical countries offer some fantastic fishing, but they also have a reputation for producing dysentary from the water. You can also contract a lesser reaction known affectionately as "Turista." If you are traveling in countries where that illness is prevalent, you should carry medication to stop the diarrhea. Some physicians also prescribe tablets that you can take prophylactically to prevent the occurrence of "Turista."

6

FIRST AID

In spite of all the precautions taken, accidents can and do happen. When they occur in the field, they are complicated by the fact that medical aid might not be as close as it is in an urban area. No outdoorsman is expected to be a doctor, but in an emergency situation, he should be able to offer whatever assistance he can. Sometimes, this first aid will spell the difference between life and death.

Few of us in the field will have the needed equipment at hand, at least not in a neat package with a complete set of instructions. Even fewer sportsmen will have a first-aid manual in their hip pocket. Unless you're a physician, you won't remember all of the symptoms and all of the treatments. Then why bother learning about first aid at all? There are many answers that could be given, all of which are true and valid. They all boil down to the fact that you will be helping another human being (and perhaps saving a life in the process). Isn't that what sportsmanship and the outdoors is all about?

A General Approach

Without practice, you're not going to be an instant expert in first aid. Not many of us have the chance to practice the techniques, so we must do the next best thing: read about them and try to keep them firmly planted in our minds. But we're not totally helpless, either. We've been blessed with common sense and judgment. These are really the cornerstones of first aid. Recognize in the beginning that every accident and every injury are unique. Since every individual is different, no two cases are precisely the same.

Your job is first to make a thorough evaluation of the situation. At times, you will be able to deliberate. In other cases, only fast and spontaneous action can save the day. I said before that you probably won't have all of the equipment you need in a neat package. That's not really important. What you have to do is start thinking. A rod case or net handle, for example, will make an excellent splint. That big red bandana you carry to wipe your brow is perfect for a bandage. A pair of waders might be just the thing to keep the victim warm. You can fashion a crude finger splint from a fly box.

Fortunately, most of the injuries sustained in the outdoors are relatively minor and the treatment will be apparent. But still, serious illnesses or injuries do occur. You must then do what is necessary until professional aid arrives. However, you should not do more than is required until help comes. As my own physician observed, "First aid is wonderful as long as you don't do the patient any harm."

What constitutes necessary and reasonable first aid will vary in each case. A great deal depends on where you are and the prospects of finding professional help within a reasonable period of time. This comes under the heading of judgment, and you alone will probably have to make the decision. So let's put it this way: Do the minimum amount necessary under the circumstances. Studies have shown that a surprising number of injured victims can survive until help arrives as long as they are not suffering from profuse bleeding, shock, or poison, and are breathing freely.

The First Anxious Moments

If you witness a serious accident or happen upon someone who has been injured afield, your first task is to carefully examine the victim. That doesn't mean you would proceed as a doctor might, but rather that you look for signs of injury. You might miss the subtle ones, but with average powers of observation, you should be able to spot the obvious ones.

Check to see if the patient is breathing and if there is severe bleeding. Either of these symptoms can cause death in minutes. Your first task is to restore breathing and/or stop severe bleeding. Which you do first (if both symptoms are present) is a matter of judgment based on the particular circumstances. But both tasks must be accomplished quickly. We'll go into detail on how to do it later in the chapter.

Next in the order of importance is to treat poisoning and then shock. If you remember nothing more than the four major emergency measures—restore breathing, stop bleeding, treat poisoning, and treat shock—you can be competent in the field. There may be time to act with other illnesses and injuries, but the top four require immediate attention. At the same time, you should send someone for professional aid. Signals that will bring help include firing three shots in rapid succession, building a smoky fire, and even using a piece of metal or a metallic flybox as a signaling mirror.

Once you have accomplished all of the critical steps that are necessary, your concern should be to make the victim comfortable and to keep him warm. Further examination can follow methodically. Another basic rule you must remember is that nothing should be poured down the throat of an unconscious person or a person who is not completely conscious. At the same time, if you suspect internal injuries, no liquids of any type should be given.

A vital function of first aid is comfort and solace to the victim. If there is a serious wound, for example, don't let the patient look at it. Continue to reassure the patient regardless of how serious the injury or illness appears. Let him know that it won't be any problem getting him out of the wilderness. If there is no one with you to go for help, you must decide whether it is better for you to go and leave the patient alone, or stay with the patient and use other means to try to get help.

Even though it can be extremely dangerous to move a patient who has sustained severe injury and broken bones, you may not have an alternative. However, keep one thing in mind: No matter how rugged or remote the terrain, medical help can get to you. If you managed to get there, others can certainly do it and bring medical assistance with them. Rescues today are made in places that were formerly considered inaccessible. In the United States and Canada, firefighters and medics can parachute into an area. You're never that far from competent help if you can get word out.

Restoring Breathing

In most cases, you have only five or six minutes to act, so don't delay. Don't worry about moving the patient unless his physical position is precarious. If so, do it quickly. Don't try to loosen clothing. Start artificial respiration right away.

A number of things will stop breathing or force breathing to become shallow and slow. Among these are drowning, smoke inhalation, electric shock, poisoning, choking, and depressant drugs. The important thing to remember is that you cannot do any harm by administering artificial respiration, but you could save a life. If the victim doesn't appear to be breathing, start respiration procedures immediately. Every second is vital!

Mouth-to-Mouth Resuscitation

Except when the victim has suffered a fractured jaw or is suffering from an extremely contagious disease, mouth-to-mouth resuscitation is the top choice of several approved methods of artificial respiration. It forces your breath directly into the victim's lungs and can be applied quickly and effectively. Mouth-to-mouth resuscitation will work on a victim regardless of age. It moves volumes of air into the lungs positively and without delay.

Mouth to Mouth Resuscitation

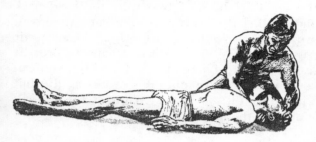

Lift victim's neck with one hand and tilt the head back by pushing it with the other hand.

Pull victim's chin up with the hand that was lifting the neck. This insures a free air passage.

Take a deep breath, place your mouth over victim's mouth and pinch his nostrils. Breathe into victim's lungs until you see his chest rise. Remove your mouth and let him exhale. Repeat as victim's lungs empty themselves for first few minutes, then 15 times per minute.

The key is to keep the air passage of the victim open at all times by tilting the head back and pulling the jaw up. At the same time, you must make sure that you block all external air passages with your mouth and hand to prevent leakage of air. Therefore, with a child, you can cover nostrils and mouth with your mouth; but with an adult, you have to pinch the nostrils shut with the fingers of one hand.

PROCEDURE

1. Place the victim on his back with the face upward.

2. Clear the victim's mouth and throat of foreign objects. Remove false teeth. Make sure tongue is not blocking air passage.

3. Tilt head of victim way back and extend jaw forward so that it juts out and lower teeth are in front of upper teeth. Head may be tilted by placing one hand under neck and lifting while pushing head back with other hand.

4. Take a deep breath and clamp your mouth tightly over the victim's to prevent air leakage. Nostrils can be pinched shut with fingers or can be closed by pressing cheek against them. If you can't get mouth open, you can administer through nostrils and hold mouth shut.

5. Blow your breath forcefully into the victim's mouth. If the victim is a small child, blow gently into both mouth and nose.

6. Watch the chest of the victim. When you see it rise, remove your mouth from his and let him exhale. At the same time, take another breath. If the chest doesn't rise, the air passage in the victim's throat is not open or air is leak-

ing out around the mouth or nostrils. Check this quickly, then continue.

7. As soon as the victim has exhaled (and you should be listening for the return rush of air), blow in the next deep breath. When you first start, and for the first several minutes, you should blow in the next breath just as soon as the victim's lungs empty. After that, follow a steady pace of between 12 and 15 breaths a minute.

Although many victims will start to breathe for themselves shortly after receiving the initial inhalations of artificial respiration, some may not. The rule to follow is that you continue giving mouth-to-mouth resuscitation until the patient is breathing for himself, a physician pronounces him dead, or he appears to be dead beyond any doubt. Remember, however, that many a drowning victim has been saved by continuous artificial respiration for a long time.

Silvester Method

There might be a reason why mouth-to-mouth resuscitation is impossible or impractical. In those cases, administer artificial respiration through the Silvester Method, following the same guidelines you did for mouth to mouth. It must be started just as quickly.

1. Place the victim on his back with arms folded across the chest.

2. Clear the mouth of obstructions and foreign matter.

3. Tilt the victim's head back to open the air passage. Extend the lower jaw.

The Silvester Method
of Resuscitation

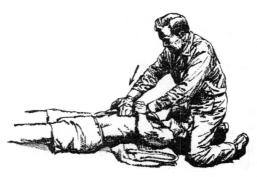

With the victim on his back, put something under his shoulders to raise them and allow head to drop backwards. Kneel at victim's head and grasp his arms at the wrists, crossing and pressing his wrists against the lower chest.

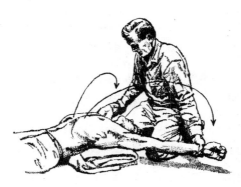

Immediately pull arms upward and outward as far as possible. Repeat 15 times a minute.

4. Place a blanket, jacket, or other support item under the shoulders to keep the head back. However, don't spend any time looking for a support item. Seconds are too precious.

5. Place one knee alongside the victim's head. You're facing toward his feet. Put your other foot alongside the other side of the victim's head.

6. Start by holding the victim's arms just above the wrist. Place his wrists over the lower ribs and lean down until you feel resistance. This will force air OUT of the lungs.

7. Now move his arms away from his body slowly, and lift them upward over his head. Keep the arms straight, forcing the chest to expand and draw air in.

8. Then, bring the arms back to his chest and start the procedure over.

9. Repeat the procedure 12 to 15 times a minute, following the same rules outlined for mouth-to-mouth resuscitation.

You can change operators without losing the rhythm by having the first man move out while continuing respiration, while the second takes the normal position. The exchange is made when the victim's arms are fully extended during the "stretch" stroke.

Stopping Severe Bleeding

Severe bleeding must be stopped at once; otherwise, the victim will be dead in three to five minutes. Arterial bleeding represents a cut or severed artery and is characterized by a substantial flow of blood coming out in *spurts*. If the

First step in stopping heavy bleeding is to apply direct pressure over the wound. If a sterile pad isn't handy, use anything that is available—a rag, fly vest, or shirt.

blood spurts, it's an artery and if it flows, it's a vein. Either is a dangerous situation. This is not the time to worry about sterile gauze pads or even infection. Your mission is to stop that bleeding.

The first step is to apply direct pressure over the wound. Grab a rag, fly vest, handkerchief, or any piece of cloth at hand and stuff it over the wound. Press firmly while you look around for additional layers of cloth. The main thing is to stop the bleeding. It cannot be emphasized enough. If cloth isn't available, use your bare hands to apply pressure.

As you add additional layers of cloth or replace your hands with cloth, don't stop the pressure. Layers of cloth should be added on top of the other layers. Nothing should be removed. When the bleeding has stopped, put more cloth on top and then bandage it. If you don't have a bandage available, tie it with strips of cloth. You'll also find that if the injury is to a limb, raising the limb higher than the rest of the body (providing bones are not broken) will help to stop the bleeding.

If pressure directly over the wound does not stop the flow of blood, your next step is to apply pressure at one of the pressure points between the injury and the heart. The femoral artery in the groin can be used to stop the flow to any point below it in the thigh or leg, while the brachial artery controls the flow of blood in the arm. It is located on the inside of the upper arm between the elbow and the armpit.

When you succeed in controlling the bleeding, you can then give the patient liquids if he is conscious and can swallow. However, do not give him alcohol, hot coffee, or any stimulant, since these liquids will increase the heart rate and the blood pressure.

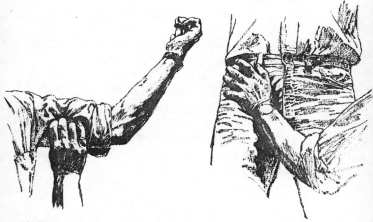

If direct pressure on wound does not stop heavy bleeding, apply pressure with fingers at either of two main points. Pressure on inner arm will stop bleeding below this point; pressure with heel of hand just below groin will stop bleeding below this point.

Tourniquet. A tourniquet should only be used if death is imminent and there is no other way to stop the bleeding. Before applying a tourniquet, you should be fully aware of the consequences. The risk of losing the limb is extremely high when a tourniquet is employed.

Let me say it again. A tourniquet is only used when all other methods of stopping a *life-threatening* hemorrhage have failed.

In recent years, medical opinion in some quarters has changed regarding how a tourniquet should be applied. It was previously believed that the tourniquet should be loosened for a few seconds every fifteen minutes or so. Many doctors now believe that once a tourniquet is applied, it should not be loosened at all. They reason that every time a tourniquet is loosened, it could dislodge clots and cause the bleeding to resume, resulting in severe shock and death.

An even more important view states that the injured tissue may release concentrated amounts of a harmful substance into the system when the tourniquet is loosened, producing an effect known as "tourniquet shock." This could prove fatal. However, it is almost certain that the tourniquet will cause the loss of the limb. Your decision to use one must weigh the loss of a limb against death, if death seems a certainty.

The fact that a tourniquet has been applied, and the time it was applied, should be marked on a tag and attached to the victim or written directly on his forehead with iodine, lipstick, felt-tip marker, or whatever is available.

Applying a Tourniquet

1. Wrap a strong, wide cloth around limb above the wound. Tie half a square knot.

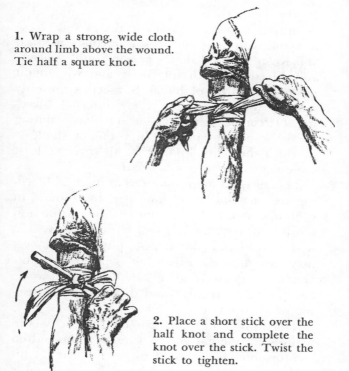

2. Place a short stick over the half knot and complete the knot over the stick. Twist the stick to tighten.

Wire, rope, fishing line, or any narrow material should never be used as a tourniquet. Instead, tear a wide strip of cloth and wrap it around the limb. Tie a half knot in it and insert a small stick. Then tie the other half of the knot over the stick and a second half knot. Twist the stick to restrict the flow of blood. Remember that the tourniquet should only be tight enough to stop the flow of blood—no tighter.

Internal Bleeding

In the field, there is practically nothing of a definitive nature that you can do, except recognize the symptoms and seek immediate medical aid. Keep in mind that a person could conceivably bleed to death internally and you might never see a drop of blood. Surgery is the only method for controlling severe internal bleeding. Of course, if you do detect blood coming from the nose or mouth, in vomit or stool, or in the urine, you know that there is at least some degree of internal bleeding.

The outward manifestations of internal bleeding are very similar to those symptoms found in profound shock. The victim will be restless and possibly thirsty, he may feel faint or dizzy, skin will be cold and clammy, the pupils of the eyes may be dilated. Breathing will be shallow and/or irregular. The pulse will be rapid, weak, and possibly irregular, and there may be a feeling of great anxiety.

The only thing you can do for the victim while someone has gone for aid is to make him comfortable. You should place him flat on his back, or slightly propped up if he has trouble breathing. Keep him quiet and reassure him. Do not give him stimulants. Other than that, you are helpless to do more.

Nose Bleed

A nosebleed is seldom serious, although it is annoying. However, a steady and prolonged flow of blood can become serious. Perhaps the most effective method of stopping nosebleed is to keep the patient in a sitting position, insert a small wad of absorbent cotton in each nostril, and gently squeeze the nostrils together for at least *six minutes*.

If the nosebleed doesn't appear serious, you might be able to stop it with thumb pressure on the upper lip just below the nose. As a word of caution, if a person has repeated nosebleeds or it becomes difficult to control the flow of blood, he should see a physician.

Poisoning

Speed is most essential in treating a person who has been poisoned. This is another emergency where first aid is vital and must be administered promptly. You must prevent the body from absorbing the poison. Many poisons contain information on the recommended antidote right on the label. If you know the poison and the antidote—and the latter is readily available—give it to the victim. Otherwise, use milk or water to dilute the poison. The victim should be given at least four or five glasses and possibly six to eight. The liquid should be taken as soon after the poisoning as possible.

If you don't see the victim take a poison or he is unconscious, you can test for poisoning by smelling his breath. Corrosive poisons also will produce stains and burns on the lips and mouth.

The important thing to remember is that when the poison is a petroleum product like gasolene or kerosene, or an acid or alkali, *do not* induce vomiting. For other poisons, do induce vomiting. Vomiting can be induced by placing a finger in the back of the victim's throat or having him drink a glass of warm water with two tablespoons of salt. Do not induce vomiting if the patient is unconscious or has a burning sensation in his throat.

It's also essential that you keep the patient's head between his knees if he should vomit, to prevent vomitus from backtracking into the lungs.

Your next move is to get a doctor on the scene or get the victim to a hospital. Save the container and any remaining poison so the medical authorities can take the appropriate action.

Skin Contamination

The antidote for a corrosive substance on the skin is water, water, and more water. Speed is also essential. The faster you dilute the poison with water, the less the chance of extensive injury. Keep pouring water on the area, even while you are moving clothing out of the way.

Shock

Shock is a complicated physiologic state that can become much more serious than the injury or accident that caused it. In fact, people have died from shock when the injury itself was not fatal. Shock is a depressed body state that can be produced by many factors. Basically, it affects the circulation of blood throughout the body and could deprive the brain and other vital organs from receiving enough blood to maintain life.

Specialists tell us that the sooner the treatment for shock begins, the better it will be for the victim. That places responsibility for initial treatment in the hands of the person administering first aid. Except in the case of a very minor injury, shock can occur. YOU SHOULD ALWAYS LOOK FOR SHOCK IN EVERY CASE. In fact, you don't have to wait for shock to develop. Start treatment on a preventative basis as long as the treatment does not interfere with other injuries or ailments.

The symptoms of shock may appear all at once or they may develop gradually. Therefore, any or all of the following symptoms may be present: The face will lose color and look pale. Skin will turn cold and clammy. Eyes may be vacant and dull with dilated pupils and drooping eyelids. There could be thirst and restlessness, a general weakness, even sluggishness. Breathing can become shallow and irregular, while the pulse is rapid, weak, and irregular. The patient may collapse or be unconscious.

One problem for the layman is that it's not always easy to tell if the victim is suffering from shock and shock alone. Many of the symptoms are identical to those exhibited by a patient suffering from internal bleeding or acute heart disease. In those cases and other ones, treatment for shock may do actual harm, even though shock may be present.

If you're certain it is shock, keep the victim lying down with his feet raised slightly higher than his head. Be careful if there are broken bones. If you do suspect heart disease, keep the victim lying flat rather than raising the legs or lowering the head. It's important to keep him warm by placing a blanket or coat under him as well as over him. Care must be taken, however, to avoid overheating. You're trying to prevent body cooling, rather than raise the temperature.

When the victim is conscious, not vomiting, and able to swallow, give him tea, coffee, water, or a special shock solution made by mixing a half teaspoon of baking soda and a teaspoon of salt to a quart of water. Again, when internal bleeding or abdominal injury is suspected, liquids should not be given.

Choking

Either food or a foreign body can lodge in the throat, blocking the air passage and making breathing difficult. Action should be taken instantly. Lower the victim's head below the rest of his body while he makes an expiratory effort to "cough" it up. If this doesn't work immediately, help him extend the jaw to open the airway. If this fails, resort immediately to mouth-to-mouth ASPIRATION. This is a new concept in which you as the rescuer use the sucking process to help pull the foreign object out. All of this should have taken less than half a minute.

Drape the patient over a chair, table, even a rock in the outdoors, and slap him sharply between the shoulder blades. Make sure his body from the waist up is hanging over the side. This should release the object. If that fails, start mouth-to-mouth resuscitation in an effort to get air into the lungs.

Heart Attack

This is a relatively common medical emergency and one that you could encounter afield. There are several types of heart disease. Some produce intense pain while others do not. As a layman in an area far from medical help, there are certain things you can do. Keep in mind that the majority of heart attacks do not produce instant death.

Heart attack victims should be placed in a half-sitting position. Do not lay the victim flat. If he is carrying nitroglycerine tablets, or they are available, place one under his tongue, even before medical assistance arrives. Otherwise, all you can do is make him comfortable, keep him warm, and wait for aid to arrive.

If breathing stops, resort immediately to mouth-to-mouth resuscitation and external cardiac massage. It will take two rescuers—one giving resuscitation and the other giving heart massage—to do both at the same time. Otherwise, massage the heart for about twenty seconds, then blow four or five deep breaths in mouth-to-mouth resuscitation, then resume heart massage for another twenty seconds. Continue the procedure until the heart resumes pumping. Then, continue mouth-to-mouth resuscitation and follow the procedure outlined under that section on when to stop.

To administer external cardiac massage, lay the patient flat on his back and kneel alongside his chest at right angles to it. Place the heel of one hand on the lower third of the breastbone. Place the heel of the other hand on top of the first. Now apply firm pressure downward, moving the breastbone from 1 to 2 inches. This will take from 70 to 90 pounds of pressure. Then, relax the hands instantly and repeat the process. The recommended rhythm is to exert pressure once each second.

Keep in mind that too much pressure can injure the ribs or the heart. The pressure should be enough to move the breastbone from 1 to 2 inches. That's all.

Snakebite

If someone is bitten by a poisonous snake, you should be able to see one or both fang marks in the skin. You might also be able to identify the snake as we discussed earlier in the book.

If you're going into snake country, you should carry an approved snakebite kit, available at most sporting goods stores.

A snakebite victim should be made to lie down immediately and remain as quiet as possible. Encourage him to stay calm. Excitement will cause the heart to pump faster and the blood pressure to increase, thus increasing the rate of poison absorption. Your first step is to put a constricting band just above the bite in the direction of the heart. You can use a triangular bandage, belt, tie, or any one of a dozen items to form the band. Remember that this is *not* a tourniquet. It should be only tight enough to stop the flow of blood in the surface veins, but not tight enough to restrict the flow of blood in the arteries or deep veins. Loosen the band at short intervals periodically.

Place a knife blade or razor in a flame to sterilize it and make an incision over each fang mark about a quarter inch deep. If you have a suction cup and a snakebite kit, you have all the necessary equipment. Use the suction cup to draw out the venom, which is mixed with blood and lymph. If you don't have a suction cup, you can suck the poison out with your mouth *providing you don't have open cuts or sores in your mouth*.

Some snakebite experts claim these two cuts are all that are necessary, while others suggest making additional cuts in the areas of greatest swelling. If the bite is in the arm or leg and the swelling creeps up under the constricting band, place another band above it and then remove the first one. Be careful when you make the incision not to go too deep and cut muscles and nerves.

Three steps in treating snakebite: tie constricting band above wound; make incisions over fang marks; apply suction cup to draw out venom.

Suction should continue for at least an hour. The patient should be encouraged to drink plenty of water to help dilute the poison. It is now believed that the application of cold water or ice helps by slowing the absorption of the poison. The body can better tolerate this poison if it trickles through in small doses.

Try to get the patient to a doctor or hospital for antivenin shots. Above all, don't forget that there are very few fatalities from snakebite, although the victim will suffer discomfort.

Removing a Fishhook

Call it an occupational hazard, but every fisherman runs the risk of imbedding a fishhook in his skin at one time or another. How you handle the injury depends on how deeply the hook has penetrated and the part of the body it has entered. If it's in a critical part of the body like the eye, put a dressing over the wound, leave the fishhook right where it is, snip off the leader, and get to a doctor if at all possible.

Fortunately, most fishhook accidents are not serious and they can be handled in the field. Obviously, if the barb has not penetrated or barely penetrated the skin, and you can back it out, by all means do so.

One of the most painful accidents occurs when you are trying to take a gang-hook plug out of a fish's mouth and the fish shakes suddenly, driving the hooks in your hand. The fish is on the other end, and his violent shaking can cause extreme pain. Your first objective here is to subdue or kill the fish quickly to avoid multiple hookings or the hooks tearing out. Once you have the fish subdued, use your cutting pliers to cut the hook or hooks that are imbedded in your hand off the plug. Then proceed with the regular hook-removal procedure.

Remove a fishhook by clipping off the barb and pulling it back through the entry hole.

As a word of caution, if you don't follow the practice of dropping the rod or "bowing" to a fish when he jumps during the battle, hold the rod slightly to the side. Then if the plug or lure comes loose, it won't spring back into your face.

Removing a fishhook is painful, but it is not complicated. There are methods for pulling it out the same way it went in even when the barb is buried, but the age-old technique seems easiest. You simply twist the hook so that it continues in as shallow a circle as possible, pushing it through the flesh until the barb emerges on the other side. Take a pair of cutting pliers and snip the barb off. Then, back the hook out the same way it went in. Let the wound bleed for a short time by squeezing it gently, dress it, and keep it covered. If you haven't had a tetanus shot in the last two years, you should get one immediately. Check on the wound periodically. It's always a good idea to see a doctor anyway, but if the wound shows signs of becoming infected, make sure you get medical attention promptly.

Eyes

If you sustain an eye injury, cover the eye with a sterile bandage and seek professional help. Don't try to treat an eye injury yourself. Should you, however, get a chemical in the eye, wash it out immediately, flushing it with plenty of water. Then bandage the eye and seek professional help.

Quite often, a foreign body enters the outside

of the eye. If you can remove it easily, do so, but be extremely careful. A foreign object can easily scratch or otherwise injure the eye and if you have trouble getting it out, bandage the eye and set off for a qualified physician.

Teeth

Before going on any type of extended trip to a remote region, have your teeth checked by your family dentist. Occasionally, a toothache may occur before you get back. Chances are you'll want to cut your trip short to seek dental assistance, but in the meantime, you can apply Oil of Cloves or hot or cold compresses as an analgesic. Aspirin will sometimes help temporarily. If a filling comes out and you have dental wax with you, you can pack the tooth with wax until you get to the dentist.

Blisters

All of us at one time or another have suffered the discomfort of a blister on our feet, caused by friction between the skin and an irritant like a pinched sock or tight shoe. If the blister can be protected from breaking, do so by covering it or removing the source of the irritation. Eventually, the fluid will be absorbed back through the skin and the foot will return to normal.

If the blister is already broken, clean it thoroughly with soap and water, and cover it with gauze and a bandage. More effort is required on a blister that is just about to break. In this case, sterilize a needle by immersing it in a flame and puncture the edge of the blister. Now press the other sides of the blister gently, forcing the fluid out of the opening you just made with the needle. When the fluid has been drained out, apply a sterile gauze pad and adhesive.

Burns

The seriousness of a burn is expressed in degrees. A first-degree burn is characterized by reddened skin, but does not produce injury to the deeper layers. A second-degree burn will blister the skin, and is slightly deeper than first degree. Sunburn can be second degree, but it is more often first degree. Either of these two degrees will heal by themselves. If treated properly, you can reduce the healing time.

A third-degree burn will not heal by itself and is among the most difficult medical problems to handle. The skin is deeply burned and often charred. Shock is present with almost any burn and should be treated. In third-degree burning, burn shock is usually present and can be fatal.

The seriousness of a burn is also measured by the area of the skin covered. Thus, you must consider both the degree of the burn and the area covered. But ascertaining the true degree of the burn is difficult and might take several days.

In any burn case, your objectives are to combat the shock that will follow, prevent the burned area from becoming infected, and control the pain. The burned area can be immersed in cold water or ice if the skin is not broken. In fact, for very minor burns, this should be the first step taken. Avoid the use of greases, oils, ointments, or similar preparations on any serious burn. Water solvent preparations may be used on first-degree burns like a sunburn.

Your first task in a serious burn case is to get the victim to a doctor or hospital, while you treat the patient for shock. If you're far from medical aid, cut the clothing away from the burned area, leaving any particles of cloth that may adhere. Cover the area completely with several layers of sterile dressing and bandage it in place. The bandage should not be tight and, if possible, should be attached to an area that is not burned. Try to keep air from reaching the burned area.

Above all, leave the area completely alone once it is bandaged and don't change the dressing. While you're applying the bandage, to avoid infection don't touch the burned area, break blisters, or even breath on the burn.

Chemical burns should be flushed thoroughly with fresh water, removing as much of the chemical as you can. Then, administer treatment as you would for any other burn.

Appendicitis

Typically, an appendicitis is characterized by abdominal pains accompanied by nausea and vomiting. The point to remember is that the pain may not shift to the right side of the abdomen. In fact, there is no infallible way of telling if the patient does have an appendicitis.

However, you can consider the possibility if some of the symptoms are met and particularly if the pain is very sharp. Yet, the pain may not be as sharp as some people believe.

Consider every abdominal pain to be serious until proven otherwise. If it persists, consult a physician at once. If appendicitis is even suspected, do not give any laxatives. That could be fatal. In the field, keep the patient in a semi-reclining position, if possible, and put a pillow under his knees to keep them flexed. An ice bag on the area may help until you can reach medical facilities.

Appendicitis should be regarded as a serious illness. The appendix can rupture and spread the infection through the body. Peritonitis can set in. But with proper medical treatment, most patients recover. Flying home from a fishing trip in Latin America not long ago, I encountered a man, accompanied by a physician, who was being transported to the United States. His appendix had ruptured in the jungle some ten days before and he was being flown to a hospital in Miami for surgery. Thus, no matter where you might be when appendicitis strikes, you have every chance to recover.

Cuts and Abrasions

Cuts and abrasions can be a by-product of life in the outdoors. Most are of a minor nature and only require treatment to prevent infection. Clean the wound thoroughly with soap and water. Stop any bleeding with a sterile gauze pad and then dress the wound.

Fractures

A fracture is the medical term for a broken bone. It is further classified as a closed or open fracture. A closed fracture is a break in the bone, but the skin has not been broken and there is no open wound. An open fracture is when a bone has pushed through the skin, creating a wound. Naturally, your first job in the latter case is to stop the bleeding.

Determining that a bone has been broken is not always easy without an X-ray, and you won't have X-rays available in the field. Nevertheless, you should treat for a fracture if you suspect the remote possibility of one. Of course, if you can see the bone, you know that it is broken. Another way of telling is to look for a deformity. All of us know the normal position of our bones and if one looks like it's deformed, it could be broken. Sometimes the victim can actually hear the bone "pop." Often a fracture is accompanied by pain, swelling, a grating feeling, and loss of ability to move the injured part.

Most fractures occur as the result of a fall or a crushing accident in which something falls on top of the victim or he is pushed up against something with force.

The cardinal rule no matter where you are or how remote the region is *never try to set a fracture yourself*. This is a job for a physician and you have plenty of time before it has to be set.

Unless there is a chance of the victim being in further immediate danger, don't move him. Even if you think you have found one fracture,

Splints for Common Fractures

Fractured Arm

Fractured Leg

Fractured Collarbone

Fractured Forearm
or Wrist

there could be more. This is the time to exhibit common sense and judgment. By moving a victim, the fractured bone could puncture a vital organ or it could cut through muscles and nerves or arteries and veins. Don't encourage the victim to sit up or stand up. Keep him exactly where he is until you have made a thorough examination.

You cannot do any harm by immobilizing an area of the body if you do it properly. That's the basic approach to a fracture. Immobilize the injured parts before you consider moving the patient. That means using splints, and a splint can be made from anything including rolled up or folded newspaper.

It's impossible in limited space to tell you the best way to immobilize each part of the body should that be necessary. But with common sense you should be able to figure it out. Fashion a splint out of anything handy. We mentioned before that a rod case, net handle, tree limb, or similar object will do nicely.

If there is an open wound, stop the bleeding and dress it before proceeding with the splinting. Then, find materials for a splint and pad them with clothing, rags, fly vest, or anything at hand. Secure the splint in at least three places. The object is to extend the splint beyond the nearest joint to prevent movement of the injured part. You can secure the splint to the victim with cloth, rags, or bandages. One strip should go around the injured part, with two more on either end of the splint beyond any joints.

After you've secured the splint, check it every fifteen or twenty minutes to make sure that swelling has not cut off circulation. If it has, loosen the splint. If swelling has gone down, you may have to tighten the splint.

Whether or not you can get the patient back to medical aid depends on the type of fracture and where it is. After splinting a broken arm, for example, there should be little problem in the victim walking out with you. However, with more serious fractures in the back, head, or legs, extreme care must be taken in moving the victim. Your best alternative is to try to get a team of trained rescuers to the accident scene. If you have to do it yourself, or with the help of other people who are not thoroughly trained, be extremely careful. In some injuries, the entire body must be supported and splinted before moving the victim. Then he should be carried in a reclining position (depending on the injuries).

If you have a canoe, you might be able to bring it to the victim by dragging it over land. Completely splinted, he could be placed in the bottom of the canoe, and the canoe dragged back to the water. Remember, however, that with fractures of such places as the back, ribs, chest (sternum), or spine, you cannot stuff the victim in a car and drive him to the hospital. He'll be much better off if he waits for adequate transportation in which he can be moved in a flat position.

Try to make the victim as comfortable as possible while you are waiting. He should be covered to help him maintain body warmth. At the same time, don't overlook the fact that shock can easily accompany any injury in which a bone is broken.

Heat Exhaustion

Fishing hard or walking in hot climates can produce heat exhaustion. In fact, just being in the heat of the day can cause fatigue, dizziness, a cold, clammy skin, and the other symptoms of heat exhaustion. The pulse may turn weak and breathing shallow. What happens is that large quantities of blood work toward the skin in an effort to cool the body. This deprives the brain of an adequate blood supply.

If someone feels faint or dizzy in hot weather, you should be alert to the possibility of heat exhaustion. Your initial aid is to get the victim to as cool and comfortable a place as possible. He should be placed in a reclining position and his clothing loosened or removed to aid heat dissipation. Cooling can be encouraged faster with an electric fan or by wiping the forehead and wrists with cold, moist towels.

Heat exhaustion sometimes indicates a depletion of salt in the body and salt tablets taken orally will help. If they are not available, have the patient drink a solution of salt dissolved in water. When the victim starts to recover, encourage him to drink plenty of liquids.

Heat Stroke

Heat stroke is much more serious than heat exhaustion and could prove fatal. It is accompanied by very high body temperature, rapid pulse, and flushed skin. Medical aid should be sent for immediately. In the meantime, your task is to try to bring the high temperature down. If you have a tub of ice and/or cold water available, use it. Otherwise, you'll have to use whatever is at hand to bring the temperature down as fast as you can. Wet sheets and towels will help. Keep the patient in a reclining position since heat stroke is sometimes accompanied by heart disease.

Frostbite

Frostbite is similar to a burn in that it involves damage to the tissues. It generally starts on the extremities—hands, feet, or facial features—as circulation is poorest in these regions of the body. Frostbite can be detected by a numbness or tingling sensation accompanied by a change of skin tone. At first, the skin may be slightly pink, but then it turns white or ashen-yellow.

When frostbite does occur, get the victim indoors as soon as possible. Cover the area with a warm hand or warm clothing taken from another area. Hands can be placed under the armpits inside the outer jacket. If lukewarm water is available, place the frostbitten area in the water. Care must be taken not to use hot water or heat lamps. Gentle heating of the area is the best remedy, but excessive heating can cause complications and is dangerous.

Once the frostbitten area has been warmed, encourage the patient to move it. He can have hot liquids to drink, but nothing alcoholic. And forget the old wive's tale of rubbing snow on frostbite. Not only doesn't it help, but any type of rubbing increases the risk of infection.

Sprains and Dislocations

A sprain is an injury to the tissues surrounding a joint, while a dislocation is a stretching of

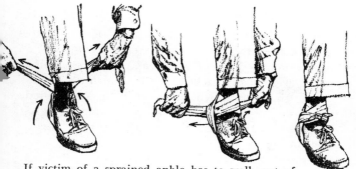

If victim of a sprained ankle has to walk out of the woods, support the ankle with a triangular bandage tied over the shoe.

the fibrous tissue capsule that holds the joint together. In a ball and socket type of joint, the ball slips out of the socket. The best policy is to treat sprains and dislocations as fractures unless you are positive that no fracture has occurred. This is often difficult to tell without an X-ray.

In the field, immobilize the joint with splints and get the patient to professional help. Making a precise diagnosis is seldom important as long as the joint is immobilized. Sometimes it is necessary to walk out with a twisted or sprained ankle. If there are no other alternatives, loosen the shoelaces to provide for swelling and strap the ankle. This is done right over the shoe and can be accomplished with a triangular bandage or strips of cloth. The application of cold compresses during the first day will help to reduce swelling and minimize any leakage of blood. If the patient doesn't have to be moved, keep the injured joint slightly above the rest of the body.

Fever

Fever is another warning signal of the body that something is wrong. It can accompany a great many illnesses and some injuries. Until the patient can reach a doctor, you must try to bring the fever down. This can be accomplished by sponging the body with cool water and giving the patient aspirin or aspirin-type medication.

If you have compiled a medical kit with your physician's help and have antibiotics with you, you may administer them based on the instructions your physician gave you.

Wounds

All of us have experience in treating minor cuts and abrasions. Wounds, however, are of a much more serious nature. A puncture wound might have a small opening in the skin but extend deeply into the tissues. With any wound, your first task is to stop the bleeding. Usually this can be done by the application of direct pressure on the wound.

If the wound is not serious, it should be cleaned to prevent infection with soap and water, taking care to delicately clean *away* from the wound. The next step is to cover the wound with a sterile dressing and bandage.

With a more serious wound, the best policy is to try to stop the bleeding, cover it to prevent further chance of infection, and get the patient to a doctor. If organs are extending through the opening, don't try to push them back in. If the wound is very deep or extensive, don't even try to clean it. Just cover the wound and get help. Suturing or closing a wound is also a job for a doctor.

Conclusion

Every outdoorsman should be well-versed in the principles of safety and first aid. Books may prove helpful but, at best, they are limited. If this book has a purpose, it is to serve as a guide in making you aware of some of the problems you may be called upon to face. Perhaps it will stimulate you to take an accredited course in safety and first aid where you will be shown in detail what actions to take.

Unless you are trained in the practice of medicine, realize that your role is to administer first aid where and when it is necessary. If you are in doubt and the situation appears serious, treat for the worst. You may be wrong, but at least you'll be on the safe side. Above all, remember that the greatest assets you have in the outdoors are judgment and common sense.

INDEX